Further into the Wilderness

The Continuing Adventures of Fur Trader Alexander Henry
Among the Native Peoples and Northern Waterways

Further into the Wilderness

The Continuing Adventures of Fur Trader Alexander Henry
Among the Native Peoples and Northern Waterways

Charles Cleland

Published by
Mission Point Press,
2554 Chandler Road
Traverse City, Michigan 49696

First Edition
Printed in the United States
Available for purchase at Amazon.com.

Library of Congress Control Number 2019917700
    ISBN: Hardcover 978-1-950659-37-1
         Softcover 978-1-950659-33-3

Cover art and sketches by artist Sharon Smithem, Charlevoix, Michigan
Map design by artist Colleen Zanotti, Traverse City, Michigan

Dedication

I would like to dedicate this work to my grandchildren Abby Cleland, Sophie Cleland, Carlisle Edenton, Madeleine Raymond, Haley Raymond, Zoe Zint, and Zac Zint.

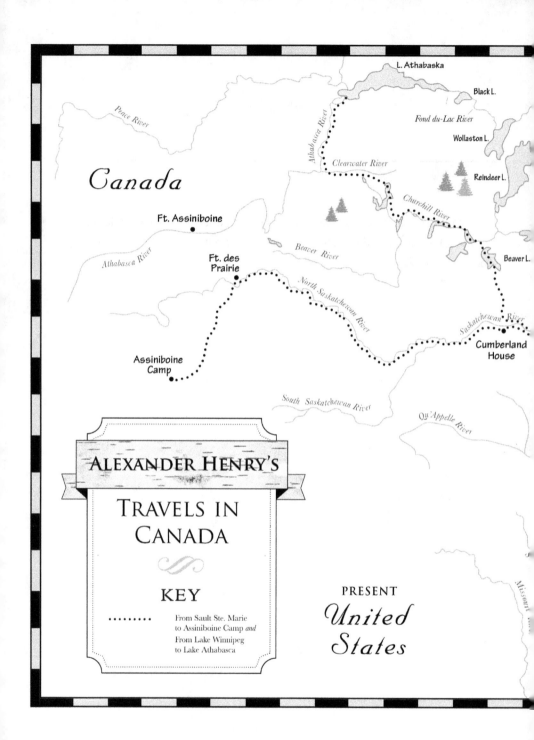

L. Athabaska

Black L.

Fond du-Lac River

Wollaston L.

Peace River

Reindeer L.

Athabasca River

Clearwater River

Canada

Churchill River

Ft. Assiniboine

Beaver River

Beaver L.

Athabasca River

Ft. des
Prairie

North Saskatchewan River

Saskatchewan River

Cumberland
House

Assiniboine
Camp

South Saskatchewan River

Qu'Appelle River

ALEXANDER HENRY'S

TRAVELS IN
CANADA

PRESENT

*United
States*

KEY

·········· From Sault Ste. Marie
to Assiniboine Camp *and*
From Lake Winnipeg
to Lake Athabasca

Missouri

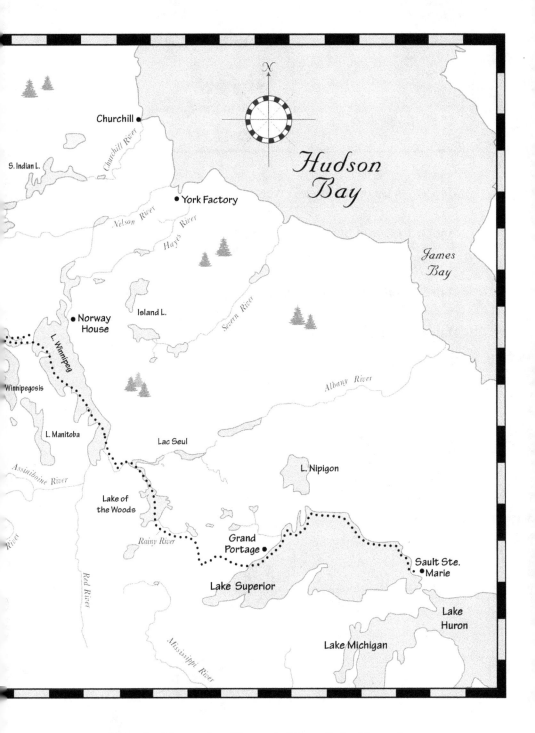

Map 1: Alexander Henry's Travels in Canada

Index of Maps

Preface

This book is based upon the real-life travels of historic figure and adventurer Alexander Henry. Henry was a noted fur trader in both the Lake Michigan and Lake Superior regions during the eighteenth century with intimate knowledge of life and cultures of native people.

Modern readers will admire Henry for his bravery and grit when facing the trials and tribulations of frontier life. Henry was a canoe traveler on the river highways and lakes of the region and also walked hundreds of miles through the immense forests and featureless prairies, in all seasons of the year. He charted the geography of much of central North America for generations of Americans and Canadians who today figuratively follow his snowshoe tracks and the wake of his canoes.

His travels took him to central and western Canada, where he investigated the many routes of canoe travel which emanate from Lake Winnipeg and from which travelers could reach every part of the North American continent. Henry wrote a memoir of his life as a fur trader which was published in 1809 under the title *Travels and Adventures in Canada and the Indian Territories between the Years 1760 and 1776*. This work was the basis for my fictionalized account of Henry's travels between 1760 and 1765 titled *Beyond the Far Horizon, Adventures of a Fur Trader*, published by Ex Libris Press in 2015.

This work of historical fiction is a sequel which follows Henry's further adventures in the Lake Superior region and Western Canada between 1755 and the War of 1812. As in my account of Henry's early years, I depicted the time and places he visited and the historic figures with whom he interacted as accurately as possible. As a work of fiction I added dialogue as well as some events of my own creation. In order to help the reader sort out my fiction from historical fact I have appended a section called *Historical*

Notes: The Real-life People and Stories Behind the Characters, to help guide in making these distinctions.

I have been long interested in writing about Henry's fascinating story for several reasons. Henry provides one of the very few first-hand descriptions of Ojibwe, Odawa, Cree, and Assiniboine cultures at the time when these people were still living from the land, speaking their own languages, and practicing their age-old cultural traditions. As an adopted member of an Ojibwe family, Henry knew and described their lives in the mid-eighteenth century from a personal perspective which is rarely available to native peoples nor to modern ethnographers.

Henry is also a person of note in both American and Canadian history. He left the only first-person account of the Ojibwe/Odawa attack against British rule and capture of Fort Michilimackinac in 1763. The uprising was part of the Pontiac Rebellion, a response by natives to new British trade policies in the area.

Henry's own account of the interesting historical and cultural details of his time is not widely available to readers today. It is my goal to embellish Henry's personal account by presenting this work in light of modern knowledge drawn from modern historians, ethologists and naturalists. I hope to better interpret Henry's contribution to our own understanding of the past and the sacrifices made by our ancestors. Henry and those like him were people of strong character and resolve, with high hopes for a good future for those they knew would follow.

Charles Cleland
Norwood, Michigan

Acknowledgments

The story of Alexander Henry, through his many adventures in various locales, renders the retelling of his eighteenth-century story somewhat of a puzzle in itself. For help in my effort to make his story understandable and available for the modern reader, I am indebted to and grateful for the good work of many people.

In regard to the narrative, I am indebted to Jennifer Carroll, distinguished editor for Mission Point Press. She not only did a great job of editing, but also made many suggestions that improved my ability to bring Alexander Henry's exploits to life.

For the portraits of the characters in the book as well as the cover art, I wish to thank Charlevoix artist extraordinaire Sharon Smithem. Her work adds visual charm to the text.

The beautiful and complex maps showing the extent of Henry's travels as they are described here, I regard as a necessary supplement to the written word. The maps were designed and produced by Colleen Zanotti of Traverse City.

Finally, I wish to acknowledge book designer Brian Grubb and Business Manager Doug Weaver of Mission Point Press. They made the writing of this book a rewarding experience.

I am also grateful to Nancy Cleland, Josh Cleland and Cathy Wigand for the time and effort they spent in proofreading the manuscript of this book.

And I'm grateful for the kindness of Diane and Bill Dupont, owners of the Round Lake Bookstore in Charlevoix, and the Charlevoix Public Library for help in launching this book.

Beyond the creation and marketing of this volume, I wish to sincerely thank my wife Nancy for help in solving a myriad of problems in organization and for her patience in dealing with my lapses while my mind took a vacation into the eighteenth century.

Characters in English or Ojibwe

*Real-life historic characters

Anagons: wife of *Miigwan*

*Athanasius: Ojibwe wife of Jean Baptiste Cadotte

*Cadotte, Jean-Baptiste: fur trader

*Champion, Etienne: fur trade agent in Montréal

*Cass, Lewis: territorial governor of Michigan (1813-1831)

*Ermatinger, Charles: Canadian Sault fur trader

*Francher, Gabriel: American Sault fur trader and merchant

*Frobisher, Joseph and Thomas: Canadian fur traders and explorers

*Great Road: an Assiniboine chief

*Henry, Alexander: fur trader and adventurer

Henry, Collin: nephew of Alexander Henry

*Homes, William: fur trader

Josette: Alexander Henry's Indian (country) wife

Kaygayosh (Gull): *Shingabawassin*'s father

*Kittson, Julia: Alexander Henry's (town) wife

Maidosagee (Loon's Foot): Chequamegon band war leader

Miigwan: Alexander Henry's Ojibwe brother

Papakin: *Miigwan*'s daughter

*Patterson, Charles: fur trader

Sassaba: son of Sunshine and Crane clan war leader

Shingabawassin (Spirit Stone): Ojibwe civil chief

Sunshine (*Zagaate giizis*): Ojibwe wife of Collin Henry

*Solomon, Ezekiel: Michilimackinac fur trader

Wawatum (Little goose): Ojibwe father of Alexander Henry

Wabigonkwe (Flower woman): Ojibwe mother of Alexander Henry

Zhigaag (Skunk): Alexander Henry's Ojibwe name

CHAPTER 1

Canoe Travelers

It was an unusually long hard winter in the Sault. Even in the very early autumn, skeins of geese and ducks crossed over the river in a virtual flood as they rode the cold north winds southward in huge numbers. Some of the old men who sat smoking their pipes took note of this harbinger of harsh weather to issue their predictions, but even now few were prepared for the brutal cold and deep snow. These conditions were the legacy of repeated battering by Arctic storms roaring in from the Canadian prairies and northern forests.

It was on just such a day there came a gentle knocking on our cabin door. My wife, Josette, opened the door to find an Indian boy who offered her a gentle smile and spoke to her in the Ojibwe language. He said he had a message for *Zhigaag*, or "Skunk," the name by which I am known among the Ojibwe people because of the white streak in my black hair. I came to the door, invited the boy inside and asked him to sit at our table. The boy of about fifteen winters was dressed entirely in deerskin except for a piece of trade blanket which he wore as a cape around his shoulders. It was immediately apparent to Josette and me that our visitor was not comfortable sitting on a chair or at a table, but it was equally obvious that the young man was not intimidated by unfamiliar surroundings. I also noted that unlike other Indian children he did not stare at us with unabashed curiosity but kept his eyes downward as a sign of respect. After we were settled at the table Josette offered the boy a cup of tea and a slice of warm pumpkin bread which he readily accepted. I asked the boy's name and learned he was called *Shingabawassin*, which in English means "spirit stone."

After a suitable interval, *Shingabawassin* said that he had come to deliver an invitation from his father *Kaygayosh*, or "Gull," to *Zhigaad* and his wife for a meeting and he proceeded to address us.

"I, *Kaygayosh*, an *ogamaw* or "chief" of the Crane clan, request that you come as my guest to my village near Whitefish Point for a meal at which time I will tell you many useful things about *Ojibwe Kitchi Gami*. A little bird has whispered in my ear that *Zhigaad* will send many canoes to *Ojibwe Kitchi Gami* this fall to collect fur and to supply the Ojibwe with much-needed goods. For this reason, I will explain the ways of the lake and its history. If *Zhigaad* wishes, we will meet when the sun is overhead two days hence."

I had been a fur trader in the upper Great Lakes country for five of my twenty-five years as well as a member of the prominent *Wawatum* family and was known to most Indians by my Ojibwe name *Zhigaag*. I was surprised and pleased to come to the attention of the famed *Ogamaw Kaygayosh*. No doubt he learned of some of my exploits, knew that I spoke Ojibwe, and that unlike some of my fellow traders I did not cheat my Indian trading partners.

I told *Shingabawassin* that Josette and I would be pleased to accept the generous offer of the famous *Kaygayosh* of the Crane clan. *Shingabawassin* took his leave to carry my message to his father, as well as a pouch of parched corn and dried venison which Josette supplied for him to eat along the way.

After the boy was gone, Josette and I discussed our good impression of young *Shingabawassin*. I complimented his self-assurance and good manners while Josette took note of his oratorical skills. She asked me if I had noticed the change in the tenor and volume of his voice when he relayed his father's invitation to give the impression that a much older man was speaking. We both predicted great things from the young lad who would one day no doubt lead the Crane clan at the eastern end of Lake Superior.

On the appointed day Josette and I dressed in our finest garments and after a daylong travel by canoe we arrived at the village of *wigwam*s slightly to the west of Whitefish Point. As we neared the sandy beach, we were met by a smiling *Shingabawassin* and by his father, *Kaygayosh*, a short, powerfully built man with a very dark complexion. His face was painted with red and green, a traditional sign of the Crane clan.

Kaygayosh invited his guests to join him under a newly constructed cedar bough arbor which was situated to provide a clear view to the open water of the lake. The lake was called Lac Superior by the French, but was known to the Ojibwe as *Ojibwe Kitchi Gami*. I was seated directly behind the fire with *Kaygayosh, Shingabawassin* sat with two clan elders to my left, and Josette joined a group of women to the right of fire.

As soon as we were seated a *Mide*, a priest of the *Midewiwin* Society, the tradition-keepers of the *Ojibwe*, approached and smudged the gathering with sweetgrass smoke. He offered a blessing which included thanks to the spirits for providing a clear day as well as an appeal for their assurance that the words spoken would carry a feeling of friendship and harmony. The *Mide* also blessed the food, which he assured the spirits would be served and consumed in a respectful way to the plants and animals which had provided it.

The preliminary formalities of the supernatural concluded, small gifts were exchanged, and the food was served. After eating, *Kaygayosh* began a long oration which told of the migration which brought the Ojibwe to their great lake. He first stated that this migration, which started far to the east at the great saltwater sea, was made by people known as the *Anishnabeg*, or the true human beings. As *Kaygayosh* told the story, at a time many, many generations ago the ancestors of the *Anishnabeg* traveled up the river which drains the Great Lakes until they came to the river which today is known as the Ottawa. They slowly followed this river north and west to Lake Huron, a journey that took several generations.

From the north shore of Lake Huron, they proceeded west to the Straits of Mackinac. Here the *Anishnabeg* split into three different groups. The first continued south down the shore of *Michigami* and were henceforth known as the Potawatomi. Another group made their villages along the north shore of Lake Huron and became known as the Odawa. The last group, the Ojibwe, continued west and north up the valley of the St. Mary's River towards *Ojibwe Kitchi Gami*.

As they traveled up this river a huge crane appeared overhead and with its loud and echoing cry called the Ojibwe to follow. When the crane saw the profusion of fish in the waters at the outlet of *Ojibwa Kitchi Gami* it circled above, indicating that the Ojibwe should establish a village at this place. These were the first Crane clan people who were also known as the *boweting inini* or "people of the falls." In later times some of the people of the falls migrated west along the north shore of *Ojibwe Kitchi Gami* as well as into the great conifer forest to the north where they became people of the Caribou, Lynx, and Pike clans of the Ojibwe.

Soon after, the great crane again appeared to the people of the falls and many of them followed the crane as it soared west along the south shore of the lake. When the great bird came to Chequamegon Bay, it again circled and the Ojibwe established another large and important village at La Pointe. These people were predominantly of the Crane family but also included members of the bear, catfish, martin, loon, and moose totems. Many others of the Ojibwe people settled along small inland lakes south of *Ojibwe Kitchi Gami* and as far west as Fond du Lac at its western end.

Kaygayosh explained that thereafter the Ojibwe claimed the entire shore and they envisioned the lake itself to be like a large lodge. In this vision the Sault formed the eastern door of the lodge and Fond du Lac formed the west door. The inhabitants of the lodge were the Ojibwe villages which occupied the shores making up the exterior walls.

Kaygayosh said that those I would be trading with were one people by their common history and culture and that their location on the lake was to be understood by the logic of their mythology.

At this point *Kaygayosh* suggested a pause for refreshments and said he had more to explain which would take us into the night. We were invited to stay. I indicated we were honored to accept his invitation.

After the pause for a dinner of whitefish, moose, corn soup, and fresh fruit we enjoyed a glorious sunset over the lake. As we watched the sun pass below the horizon and as the sky bloomed with pink and lavender clouds, *Kaygayosh* began to explain some of the hazards for travelers on the lake. At the far end of *Ojibwe Kitchi Gami* live the Dakota who, he said, are a cruel and warlike people who have been fighting the Ojibwe for years. What started as a blood feud many years ago has become a war over a rich hunting territory that both tribes claim as their own. *Kaygayosh* warned me not to trade with the Dakota, which he said the Ojibwe would consider a very hostile action, especially if the trade supplied the Dakota with guns.

Alex Henry

He continued with a travel warning about the beautiful sandstone cliffs along the shore of the lake between his village and Grand Island. Travelers passing this place must be sure that waves from the north do not trap their canoes against the walls of rock since there are very few places to land. If travelers become trapped in this way the waves will destroy their canoes and all that they carry.

Finally, *Kaygayosh* reminded me not to neglect to make proper sacrifices to the underwater panther *Michipishiew* who, he said, is especially active on the north shore of the lake near Agwaw Bay. The likeness of this dreaded spirit was recently drawn on a cliff face by a returning war party. With this good advice we retired for the night to a *wigwam* to which we were directed. I had of course spent many nights in the *wigwams* that I shared with the *Wawatum* family during the year I spent traveling with them on their seasonal rounds, and I was happy to become reacquainted with the sounds, smells and warm feeling of this traditional Ojibwe home. Like most, we found the Ojibwe *wigwams* to be very neat and clean. The house floors are typically covered with woven reed mats which in turn are covered with hides and furs and arranged around the central fire pit, giving the home a very cozy feeling. In the *wigwams* people have accustomed places to sit and sleep depending on their age and gender, their personal belongings are kept in those spaces as well. All manner of items are hung from the ceiling, which frequently include bundles of herbs and medicines. These give the home the sweet smells of wintergreen, bearberry, mint, sweetgrass, and cedar. Of course, the smoke of the fireplace adds the pleasant smell of wood smoke to the entire household. *Wigwams* lack doors, so an opening is covered with a piece of fabric or an animal skin, which can be drawn aside to admit sun light. Josette and I much enjoyed the feeling of security and intimacy that came back in the *wigwam* provided.

As we were preparing for a return to the Sault the next morning, *Kaygayosh* paid a surprise visit and asked me for a favor. He said that as part of *Shingabawassin's* education for the world of the future he wanted him to learn to speak the white man's talk as well as to become acquainted with its customs. He asked me if Josette and I would be willing to accept *Shingabawassin* as an *inawemagan*, or a "relative." He also requested that the young man be permitted to live and travel with us during the coming summer and winter so that we could be his *kikinoamagejig*, or "teachers." After a brief conference Josette and I said we would enjoy having *Shingabawassin* as a member of our family and we would keep him safe. We said we would send him a message when our travel plans were finalized.

Yet another surprise awaited us as we returned to the Sault. As we approached, we observed the tall mast of a sailing ship along the river below the falls. When we neared the place where it was moored, I recognized my nephew Collin who had traveled to the Sault on the ship and was now among the crowd gathered to marvel at such a large vessel.

CHAPTER 2

The Sault

Collin: I recognized Uncle Alex at once as he pushed his way through the crowd gathered around the "Crow," the ship which had brought me to the Sault from Detroit. At first, I thought he might have forgotten his offer to teach me to be a fur trader. He pumped my hand and greeted me with assurance.

"Well, our apprentice clerk Collin has arrived! We are happy to welcome you to the Sault," he said.

Uncle Alex introduced me to his wife Josette, who greeted me with enthusiasm. I was surprised to see that Josette was an Indian but I also noticed that all the women gathered were Indians as were the great majority of the men. It was clear that no one was speaking English except for the sailors busy unloading cargo from the Crow. I could only hear French and the Indian languages and a great deal of cursing in English from the sailors.

Alex and Josette helped me carry my gear to a newly constructed building which Alex said was our company store, warehouse, and my quarters. We entered through a heavily locked door into a room lined with shelves which contained bolts of cloth, folded blankets, hanks of colorful glass beads, axes, knives, fire steels, spools of ribbon, metal buckets, files, awls, shirts, and many other items. Beyond the store, there were two other rooms. One, the warehouse, was very large and virtually empty, the other was small, with a bed, stove, a table, chairs, and several cupboards.

"This will be your quarters, so make yourself comfortable and when you are settled come to our house just down Water Street. It's the only house with a window box although it is still too cold for flowers," Uncle Alex said.

I bid Alex and Josette goodbye and started to make myself at home. Although my room was small it seemed like a palace compared to my accommodations on the Crow which consisted of a canvas hammock slung in the ship's hold among the crates and barrels which constituted the ship's cargo. Between the rolling and pitching of the ship and the damp cold, I only managed to sleep when I was utterly exhausted. Although I was used to a soldier's food, the shipboard fare which I shared with the crew was truly awful. The staple was stale biscuits infested with mealworms and potato soup with salt pork cooked over a small open fire kindled on a brick surface built into the floor of the hold.

After a nap, I found my way to Uncle Alex and Josette's home and was surprised to discover their house crowded with people. I was soon introduced to those present whose Indian names I could not pronounce or remember for long. Uncle Alex's Indian family included his father *Wawatum*, his mother *Wabigonkwe*, and his older brother *Miigwan,* and his brother's wife *Anangons* as well as their three-year-old daughter *Papakin*. Also present were their neighbor and trade partner Jean-Baptiste Cadotte, his Indian wife *Athanasius,* and several of their children. The house was hot and crowded but everyone was having a good time and although I could not understand a word of Ojibwe, Uncle Alex and *Miigwan* were competent translators and helped me interact with the other guests. This was my first social contact with Indians, but I soon learned that they were a very congenial and good-humored people. As I came to feel more comfortable with this new Indian family, I began to see that they were in most ways like any American family enjoying each other's company. I thought, with shame, of the time I told Uncle Alex that I wanted to join the military to kill Indians. I could see now that that was a very stupid and horrible thing to say.

I was particularly taken by little *Papakin*, who held her arms out to me to be picked up. When I was carrying her, she chatted away at me in Ojibwe baby talk. I could not understand her but she seemed to not be deterred except for a puzzled look on her little face when I replied in English, which she of course could not understand.

Not having any prior social interaction with Indians, I was anxious not to unknowingly transgress social mores or taboos by asking inappropriate questions. Nonetheless I found myself to be very curious about Uncle Alex's wife Josette, who in several ways seemed to be quite different from the Ojibwe women who populated the Sault. At one point in the evening I went outside with Uncle Alex to help him bring in firewood. I took the occasion to ask him about her background.

He said Josette was born a member of the Ponca tribe, which lived on the prairies west of the Mississippi River. She was captured as a young girl by Illinois Indian slave raiders and was taken across the mighty river and sold as a *pani*, or Indian slave, to a woman of an eastern tribe where she was beaten often with a rawhide quirt. After two years of abuse, she was sold to a French trader named La Vake, who also treated her very cruelly. La Vake took her to Fort St. Joseph at the south end of *Michigami* where she lived a while and was given the name Josette and learned the French language. During her captivity with La Vake, Josette spent most of her time skinning animals for the trade. At some point La Vake took Josette to Fort Michilimackinac for the annual trade rendezvous where he lost her in a Indian gambling game to Msr. de Langlade. She became a *pani* in his home which, as luck would have it, was next door to the house Uncle Alex rented. They met, fell in love, and eventually Uncle Alex bought Josette from de Langlade for a pair of dueling pistols. Uncle Alex said he would always protect her. They are partners in life, love, and he could not have found a kinder or gentler person. It is a wonder to him he found her given the hardships she endured. She is happy now and so is he.

At evening's end Uncle Alex asked me to meet him just after sunrise so he could start instructing me on my duties as the clerk and local agent for our fur trade enterprise. When we met, Uncle Alex gave me several ledger books in which I was to keep track of all aspects of the business. He started by telling me to call him either Alex or *Zhigaag*. He then explained that our company was composed of several partners which would be trading under his exclusive license for the entire Lake Superior region. Other than himself the partners of the Henry and Cadotte Fur Company included Etienne Campion, our agent in Montréal, who wholesales our furs and trans-ships our trade goods to the Sault or to Fort Michilimackinac. The fort is located at the Straits of Mackinac, which is the hub for the entire Great Lakes fur trade. Other partners of our company included Jean-Baptiste *Cadotte*, who would conduct the trade in the St. Mary's River Valley and adjacent parts of the Upper Peninsula of Michigan. *Wawatum* and his family would work out of this same area to acquire food and supplies for our paid Canadian *engagées*, or hired employees. The *engagées* would carry the trade to various Ojibwe band villages in the Lake Superior basin. Alex himself along with *Miigwan* were our field agents and responsible for developing trade relationships and solving any problems which might occur in the back country. The final partner was me, whose duties were to supervise the store and warehouse and keep careful records of all trade transactions. Alex said that profits would be split equally among the six partners.

Alex explained that my new duties will include keeping track of the trade goods which will be disbursed by our Canadian *engagées* to individual Indian trappers. There will be credit to be repaid with the furs that will come to us in the spring to pay the debts of each individual. All this is the most important job of the entire Lake Superior enterprise, but I did not really appreciate how complex the job was at that point.

Alex said that the entire Great Lakes fur trade system was not based upon currency but the equivalent worth of various furs on the market at Fort Michilimackinac. For example, at the present time, beaver was priced at two shillings and sixpence per pound, otter skins were valued at six shillings each, martin skins were worth one shilling and sixpence. Since there is no currency in circulation, Alex said if I wished to go to a drinking establishment I should take a martin skin to pay my bill.

For a more practical example, Alex said that to conduct our trade on Lake Superior in the coming season he purchased trade goods and supplies at twelve months' credit. This amount composed the freight of four canoes at the price of ten thousand pounds weight in good quality beaver. To carry these goods to the wintering grounds, he engaged twelve men at one hundred pounds of beaver per man. In order to provision these men, he also purchased forty bushels of dried corn at ten pounds of beaver per bushel.

"This is a complicated system and it will be your job to keep track of the goods which go out on credit and the furs which come back in payment," Alex said. "This will be done in one of your ledgers. In another ledger please make a record of over-the-counter transactions in your store. Since this is also on a credit system you will have to record the name of each customer and the items given to them on credit or the items taken by you in exchange. The latter could be in pelts or goods or even services, for example dried fish, firewood, or labor. These records you will keep separate in the store ledger."

"Another part of your job will be to keep the warehouse inventory, which will be eventually packed with fur waiting to be shipped by canoe to Montreal. You will keep these records in the third ledger," Alex said.

He told me I needed to have some basic skills to be a fur company clerk.

"First of all, you must know how to identify the pelts from different animals, how to grade their quality, and how to make sure they have been properly prepared in order to prevent spoilage. In addition, you will need to know some of the Ojibwe and French language to deal with your customers and to record their names in your ledger."

A wave of self-doubt swept over me. Perhaps seeing my expression Alex assured me that I would do fine with a little experience, but I was not so sure.

Before Alex went about his own business he said, since they would not be very busy over the next month, he was going to send me on an errand with *Miigwan*. The two of us would blaze a trail through the forest from the Sault to Point St. Ignace at the Straits of Mackinac opposite from Fort Michilimackinac. The purpose of this was to provide a winter route to Michilimackinac after the lakes and rivers freeze if necessity requires travel to that place during the winter season. A secondary but very important purpose was for *Miigwan* to teach me how to survive in the north woods and how animals are trapped, and their pelts prepared for the trade. Alex said we would leave in two weeks and be gone for a month.

Alex suggested that I familiarize myself with Sault Ste. Marie and to introduce myself to some of his residents so that I would become known to the people. I began my tour by exploring Sault Ste. Marie that afternoon. The first thing I discovered is that 'The Sault," as it was called by the family comes from the French word for "rapids." In this sense there are really two Sault Ste. Maries, both small towns on each side of the St. Mary's River. One is in American territory and the other is in British territory. At the foot of the rapids, is the beginning of the St. Mary's River which has its origin at the base of a twenty-foot-high rocky ledge that receives the outflow from Lake Superior. The falls and rapids below the outlet roars continually as the water flows around many small rocky islands. On most days, a rainbow-filled mist hangs over the rapids.

On the south bank, called the "American Sault," there seemed to be two neighborhoods. The first was made up of rude shacks built of scrap lumber and driftwood which lined the riverbank. These were the homes of Indian fishermen and the small space between the houses were littered with canoes, hoop nets and other fishing equipment.

In the other neighborhood, farther from the river on higher ground, houses were built in the French style with cut lumber or hewn logs called *poteaux sur sole* and *poteaux en terre*. These were laid out in rows and evenly spaced, leading me to believe that they were built on larger, private lots. These homes were mainly occupied by large *Métis* families in which the husband is either French Canadian or *Métis*, and the wives are either Ojibwe or *Métis*. When walking in this neighborhood, one is soon surrounded by smiling children who have learned to run after strangers shouting "*boo shoo Monsieur*" and hold up their little hands for a treat. I made a mental note to purchase plenty of peppermint candies for my store.

As I was returning to my room, I happened to encounter two sailors of my acquaintance from my voyage on the Crow and they invited me to accompany them to a grog house which they visited on previous voyages to the Sault. Having no other engagements nor English speakers to talk to I consented. A sign over the door of the drinking establishment, which in truth was a one-room shack, said Jacques Chambre. The interior was dark and as we entered from the bright sunshine the interior gloom was nearly impenetrable. Once my eyes adjusted, I made out a serving bar manned by a short *Métis* wearing a long dirty apron who greeted us with a silent stare. I assumed this was Jacques. There were three other patrons in the room of which two were passed out, one in a chair and the other crumpled on the floor. A third customer eyed us with wary bloodshot eyes.

Jacques Chambre reeked of rum, tobacco smoke, and body odor. One of my sailor friends, Billy, ordered a round of rum at the bar. The other friend named Tom and I found a seat on a bench. The rum served from dirty tin cups was somewhat watered but was still strong enough to burn its way down my gullet. After several rounds of drinks, Tom began to sing sea shanties and Billy began to clap and dance energetically but increasingly erratically in the small space between benches. It was not long before Billy tripped over the drunk sleeping on the floor and fell into the bar patron who was still partially conscious and pushed him to the floor. Offended by the collision he staggered to his feet and struck Billy a roundhouse blow on the side of his head. Tom leaped to the rescue of his assaulted crew mate but missed his target and slammed into the bar, upsetting a small keg of rum and then stumbling, unseating the other sleeping drunk. Just then I saw Jacques wading into the pile of struggling cursing men. He was swinging a stout club and screaming *"imbéciles"* at the top of his voice.

Although my own judgment was impaired, I realized I did not want to have my first day in the Sault end with a broken skull from joining a senseless bar fight. With all the others in the room otherwise occupied, I slipped out the door into late afternoon sun.

CHAPTER 3

Blazing a Trail

On a Monday morning in mid-May *Miigwan* and I were summoned to meet with Alex in regard to our duties over the next month or so. When we were gathered, Alex was all business and began by giving lengthy instructions to *Miigwan* in Ojibwe. Since we all spoke English, I thought this unusual but since I knew he was telling *Miigwan* what to do with me, I supposed he just didn't want me to know the details. He then explained my part in English.

"Collin, *Miigwan* will teach you how to live in the woods, how to track animals, to avoid leaving a trail, how to trap and skin fur-bearing animals and he will start teaching you the Ojibwe language," Alex said. "In turn I want you to pay attention to *Miigwan* at all times since he is my trusted and experienced *nissaaie*, or older brother."

As we parted Alex pulled me aside and told me he was going to loan me his Pennsylvania long rifle and war axe that had been my father's. He also loaned me a fine collapsing mariner's spyglass. He told me that he treasured these possessions and that I was to bring them back in good condition.

I spent the rest of the day packing my few possessions including my sleeping roll and some new items *Miigwan* supplied to me including moccasins, a pair of deerskin pants, and shirt which he said would be more comfortable and less noticeable in the woods.

Miigwan and I set out in a canoe going west along the south shore of the big lake. We had not proceeded far when *Miigwan* stopped paddling. I also stopped and, as we drifted, I looked back at *Miigwan* in the stern of the canoe and saw that he was dripping wet. He asked me if I had ever paddled a canoe before.

"No, but it seems fairly simple," I said.

"Well learning to be a good canoe man is not so simple," he replied. "It takes time. Let's start by trying to keep me dry. Each time you finish your paddle stroke you are bringing up your paddle, so it is flat to the water and that brings up water which splashes on the person in back of you. If you twist your paddle just as you finish your stroke, so the edge of the blade is up and down, it won't pick up water and I will be dry and happier."

With that we resumed paddling. A short time later we came to the mouth of a river which *Miigwan* called the *Pississowining*. Here we landed, unloaded and stashed our canoe, shouldered our packs and proceeded to follow the right bank of the river toward the south.

Miigwan: As I followed Collin along the path beside the river, it was like following a herd of elk. His heavy, stiff boots left huge prints in the softer earth and he seemed to break every plant as he passed. "What have I done to my little brother *Zhigaag* that he would send me into the woods for many weeks with a complete novice?" I asked myself. Then I remembered my father *Wawatum* had taken *Zhigaag* into the woods when he was just as unprepared. He had proven himself to be a good student and maybe Collin would learn as well.

As we moved through a thicket a partridge exploded into the air with enough noise to startle us both.

"*Gaagashkoo* or "partridge," I said, indicating the flying bird by pointing with my chin. I asked Collin to repeat the word in Ojibwe several times and he did a reasonable job. But when I asked him again an hour later, he only uttered the first sound of the word, so I asked him to repeat it many times. As we walked along, I introduced Collin to the Ojibwe words for several kinds of trees as well as any animal we encountered.

Collin: We had not gone far on our expedition when I suddenly understood why Alex sent me into the north woods with *Miigwan*. While this region may seem to some as an empty wilderness, to an Ojibwe like *Miigwan* it was a beautiful and peaceful place, full of history, the whole a priceless gift from *Kitchimanitou* "god." A small, round hill to me was much different in *Miigwan*'s world. The hill, he said, was actually a giant beaver lodge originating in the time that the creator spirit *Nanabozho* traveled the world creating each and every thing we experience today as elements of nature. For the Ojibwe, the world is filled with the abodes of various spirits, some helpful to humankind and others capable of bringing disaster to modern residents or travelers. In the Ojibwe culture the natural, supernatural, and historical places all merge into a single wonderous landscape.

Miigwan: Within a few miles from its mouth, the river took a sharp turn to the southwest. I decided to start leaving blaze marks to mark our trail to the Straits of Mackinac opposite Fort Michilimackinac. My first step was to show Collin how to make a blaze by using his war axe to cut a large piece of bark off the tree to leave the white inner wood exposed. The blazes would be at least shoulder high and should face the river, so they would be visible to those following the bank as well as those walking down the river on snowshoes when it was frozen. We placed a blaze every several hundred paces apart. Rivers are the traveling byways in the north woods in both summer and winter.

Over the next several days we made good progress even though the river was getting smaller and smaller and the ground somewhat swampy. The river finally split into three branches, and following *Zhigaag's* instructions we followed the south branch of the *Pississowining*.

When we camped at night, I continued to quiz Collin in Ojibwe. He was slowly adding words to his vocabulary. I also finally succeeded in convincing him to trade his white man's boots for moccasins, and he grudgingly agreed that they were far more comfortable although he did justly complain that they got wet very easily. Sometimes I was a trickster in teaching him animal names. For example, I asked him which animal could fly faster, *gaagashkoo* or *makwa*? He should have responded *gaagashjkoo* the partridge since *makwa* the bear couldn't fly at all.

When we decided to camp one evening, I posted Collin a short distance away on a large deer trail with his long rifle and instructions to kill a small doe. I proceeded to set up our camp and decided to take a nap. I was awakened by a rifle shot and before long Collin appeared caring his quarry over his shoulder. As it turned out Collin had grown up on a farm, so he knew the basics of butchering and set about dismembering the little doe without instructions from me. We feasted on fresh deer meat that night and for the next several days we were glad for the change of diet from dried corn and jerky.

After dinner Collin asked me why I had not given him the Ojibwe word for deer, so I complied, "*waawaashkeshii.*" One day as we approached a burnt-over clearing, we saw a large bear ripping apart rotten logs and turning over huge stones in order to find grubs. We stood inside the tree line marveling at the bear's enormous strength when suddenly the beast rose on its hind legs and began moving its head side to side sniffing the air. Clearly, he had caught our scent and was trying to locate its source. I quickly stepped into the open and the bear looked directly at me. In a few minutes his curiosity was satisfied, and he went back to foraging. Later I explained to Collin that the bear, not being able to see us, would have followed his nose until he knew what and where we were. That could have put us in danger but now the bear saw us and decided we were not a threat.

"*Makwa* has weak eyesight but a tremendous sense of smell," I said.

We continued with our blazing project going south and slightly west until we came to a stream that I told Collin was the upper reaches of the *Zhiingwaak*, or Pine River. We made good progress following the Pine until we reached its mouth on St. Martin's Bay on the Lake of the Huron. We discontinued blazing at this point because any traveler would be able to follow the lakeshore a short distance south to the Straits of Mackinac. From there the large Fort Michilimackinac could be clearly seen on the south shore and in the winter could be reached by walking across on the ice.

Our major task was completed and I told Collin we would be turning our attention to the trapping and the preservation of fur. I led us overland to the southwest where I knew from previous visits to this region there were several small inland lakes. During the next two days of travel I kept up a steady stream of questions about Ojibwe names. Although Collin was making progress I realized he had a very long way to go before he would be ready to deal with Ojibwe customers in our store.

Eventually I found a small lake that was very close to the shore of *Michigami* and had signs of beaver activity, with many cut and gnawed aspen trees near the water. There was also one large beaver lodge along the east shore. Between the lake and *Michigami* a series of high parallel sand ridges were covered with scrubby pine, cedar shrubs, and much bearberry.

North of the dunes the ground was low and swampy, a good trapping ground for muskrat and mink.

After making camp I took Collin on a tour of the beaver works and explained various trapping techniques. I found a trail between the aspen grove where beavers were working and the little lake. There was a clearly visible runway on the shallow lake bottom where the trail ended and it was here that I decided to set a trap. We waded out to where the water was about three feet deep so we would not leave human scent along the shore that would disturb the beavers and eventually came to the beaver run. Near the shore we cleared a flat spot for the trap in about four inches of water. We extended the trap chain full-length into the deeper water where we securely fastened the chain ring to a stake that we drove deep into the bottom.

The bait for the trap was a substance called castoreum which is obtained from a beaver's scent glands. I brought a supply of this substance in a small bone container. I stuck a willow branch bait stick in the bank extending out over the trap set and placed a dab of castoreum on the stick.

The scent of castoreum was irresistible to the beaver. We hoped to catch more than one and knew the animals would approach the set from deeper water, come near the bank and extend their noses to the castoreum. In the process they would place one or both feet onto the trap pan which sprang the trap jaws on the animal's front leg. The beavers would then dive into deeper water until reaching the end of the trap chain, carrying the heavy trap which would eventually take the beavers to the bottom where they would drown.

After making the first set I asked Collin to find two more places he thought might be frequented by *amikwag*. I asked Collin to return to our camp while I looked around at our surroundings.

Although this was a remote spot and not near any native villages that I knew about, it was wise to be cautious when traveling through unfamiliar territory. What made my scouting trip more immediate was that as I was going around the end of the lake earlier in the day, I noticed a patch of cattails that did not look natural. When I examined it further, I saw that someone had been harvesting cattail stalks by pulling up the newly emergent stalks to get the tender bottom which was white, crisp and good to eat even though a little slimy. In so doing, the harvester had of necessity discarded the tops of the stalks which was what caught my eye. I looked closely and found several fairly fresh moccasin prints which were small in size so were made either by a woman or young adult. I tried to follow the tracks but soon lost them, leading me to believe that the person was being careful to hide the trail.

All the more curious, I carefully began to circle out from where I lost the trail and then back towards the general westerly direction in which the person seemed to be headed. My first circuit led me into the sand hills where I picked up the faint trail. Now, moving with extreme caution I eventually came to a narrow valley between the dunes where I saw in the distance a single *wigwam*. I found a spot where I could observe the small camp without being seen. At first the place seemed deserted but after a time I saw a young woman emerge from the *wigwam* and begin cooking over a low, smokeless fire. I didn't see any other people but, although I was far away, I thought I heard her talking to someone in the *wigwam*. I decided that I should return to our camp and share this discovery with Collin.

When we met, I told Collin about the camp and of seeing only a woman, but I also told him of my suspicion that there may be another person because I heard talking. We decided that we would deal with our beaver sets in the morning and then watch the camp in the late afternoon in order to make sure that it contained no threat for us.

When we visited our traps the next morning, we were happy to discover that we caught two beavers. They were both adults, but the pelts were not in prime condition as we were trapping late in the season. Collin watched me as I skinned one of the animals, and I showed him how to slit the skin from the animal's chin down the belly to the base of the tail. From this cut slits were made down the inside of each leg and the feet were removed, likewise cuts were made around the neck and at the base of the tail. The tail was removed and would serve as our dinner. Much care must be taken in removing the pelt with a knife, which is inserted between the body fat and the underside of the skin. This must be done without cutting the skin. After the pelt was removed, we scraped the underside with a sharp knife to remove all of the fat and muscle tissue, because if not removed it would

CHARLES CLELAND

rot and damage the pelt by causing the fur to drop.

Once Collin skinned his beaver under my close supervision, I cut two flexible willow sticks that I bent into a circle and tied to form a hoop. I then used an awl to make holes around the margin of the pelts and showed Collin how to use a cord to tie and stretch the pelt within the hoop. We left the hoops, skin side up in the sun so that they would dry. This finished, we completed our trapping and skinning assignment and pulled our other traps since our purpose was not to make fur but to teach Collin how it was done.

By midafternoon we approached the mysterious *wigwam,* and I placed Collin in a spot where he could use his spyglass to get a closer look at the camp. He could clearly see the woman with his glass and began describing his observations to me. The first thing he told me was that the woman was very beautiful. She was about his own age and of average height and unlike many Ojibwe woman was slim. It was quite obvious from her movements that she was both graceful and very strong. Also, unlike the style used by most Ojibwe woman, she did not wear long braids. Her hair was cut short and hung at shoulder length. Her clothing was typical: she wore a soft deerskin skirt which came just below her knees and her lower legs were covered by leggings. Her upper body was covered by a calico trade shirt and a shawl which hung loosely about her shoulders. Except for silver ear bobs, she wore no jewelry.

I noticed that as Collin watched the woman through the spyglass he started to smile and then to laugh. "What's so funny?" I asked. Collin replied that he had solved the mystery of her talking to someone. "She has pets," he said. He told me that as she was working, he saw a gray fox come out of the woods and went straight up to her for a treat. It was clear she was chatting away at the creature and had a big smile on her face. Later a large raven flew in and perched on a branch near her. She also had a conversation with the bird, which did not appear to be tame, but neither was it shy of her.

Collin and I returned to our camp and discussed what to do about the lone woman. I told him that her circumstances were very risky since it was impossible for a lone person to survive long without the support of kin, especially if they did not have a gun to hunt. I suggested that we talk to her and Collin agreed. We decided to approach her the next day in full view so that our presence would not frighten her. I reminded Collin that she might have a gun in the *wigwam*, so we should be very cautious.

The next day in mid-morning we walked down the valley toward her *wigwam* and could see her cutting firewood. When we were a distance away we stopped, and I shouted *aaniin* or "hello." The woman was clearly startled and stopped her work, looked us over and then replied *boozhoo* and added *gigiishkaabaagwe'ina* "Are you thirsty?" I replied *enh-enh* or "yes." She beckoned us to approach. As I had instructed, Collin kept his eye on the door of the *wigwam*, but no one emerged.

We seated ourselves around her small fire, and I began a conversation with her in Ojibwe while Collin sat looking around. Since he could not understand our conversation, he soon became bored. I told the woman our names, where we lived and asked her name which she said was *Zagaate giizis,* or in English, "Sunshine." As Collin and I agreed later she was well named, she had the biggest and brightest smile either of us had seen. We also agreed that her smile only added to her physical beauty. *Zagaate giizis* served us herbal tea, a very refreshing Ojibwe courtesy.

I finally asked her how she came to be living alone in this out-of-the-way place. She told me that when she was fishing, a storm came up suddenly and blew her canoe out into the lake. The wind drove her ashore not far from where we were, and she had no idea where she was.

I told her what we were doing and that we would be in the area for a week or so. She invited us to move our camp closer to hers since she was glad for our company. After a few pleasant hours we returned to our camp. That evening we talked over our impressions of Sunshine. Collin was taken with her, but I remained suspicious. For one thing, I did not believe her story of being cast adrift in a storm. Most people who go fishing don't take all manner of camping gear such as axes, cooking vessels, pot hooks, fire starting materials and several boxes and woven bags which we observed around her camp. My conclusion was that she was prepared to be living alone for reasons we had not discovered. In other words, she was hiding. I told Collin that if we searched, we would probably find her canoe cached along the lake shore.

The following day we moved our camp to the head of her little valley

and again went over to Sunshine's camp where we were treated to one of her warm and welcoming smiles. We shared some fresh deer meat with her which she relished. Since she didn't seem to have a gun she had probably been living on plant foods except for whatever small animals she may have caught with a snare.

I continued to discuss her circumstances and after getting to know her better, I told her that her shipwreck story was implausible. When confronted with evidence she became very upset and retreated to her *wigwam*.

Sunshine: After *Miigwan* told me of his suspicions I knew it was dangerous for me to reveal my true circumstances to these two nearly complete strangers. What *Miigwan* told me about my prospects for surviving the winter here by myself were true yet I didn't know what else to do. I couldn't return to the village where I lived with my husband or I would surely be killed to avenge him. Neither could I go to the village of my father where my husband's kin would certainly look for me. If I went to any other Ojibwe village I would only be a burden.

It had occurred to me that *Miigwan* and Collin might take me with them when they returned to the Sault, but why would they help me if they didn't know my problem or the risks they would be taking by helping me? I must have seemed like a crazy woman to them. I could tell that Collin liked me and was concerned about my welfare and he would probably do what I asked of him. But *Miigwan*, although a kind man, was very suspicious of me and sensed that there were serious circumstances surrounding my situation. It was apparent to me that *Miigwan* was not only the leader of the two but was also the wiser and would not be tricked into getting involved in something he did not understand.

As I came to this realization, I knew that I could not ask or expect help from my new friends unless I told them the truth about how I came to be living here alone. I felt very worried about telling them however, since they didn't really know me and might have thought I was a liar and a murderer. They very well might have packed up and gone, leaving me to my fate.

Having decided to tell them my story for better or worse, I began to think of ways to reveal my secret. As I arranged the words in my head, they all seemed inadequate to express my shock and sorrow for the killing and for the intense fear that caused me to flee and hide. I struggled with words all night but awoke with the resolve to tell them the truth.

The next evening, I again shared dinner with *Miigwan* and Collin and despite all my planning about how to tell my story in its best light, when I began my words just came tumbling out. Since I wanted Collin to understand my true story, I asked *Miigwan* to translate my words into the white man talk so he would know the truth as well.

"Yes, I am hiding because of a tragic mistake," I said. "My husband was cruel and often got drunk. When he came home one night he threatened to kill me and began to push, slap, and kick me. I was sitting on the ground making a pair of moccasins using a sharp awl. When he kicked at me, I swung hoping to ward off the blow but the awl in my hand struck him in his upper thigh. It went very deep and when I pulled it out blood was gushing out like a river. I tried but I couldn't stop the flow and he soon died from loss of blood."

"I didn't know what to do. Since like all married Ojibwe women I was living among my husband's kin, and I knew that when they found out I had killed him that they would take revenge on me for killing their brother. It was then I decided to escape, and that night, before anyone discovered the body, I loaded up what I needed in a canoe and paddled off, and here I am. I am still afraid they will find me and kill me, and I'm also afraid that if they don't find me they will seek revenge by killing my father and my brother. I just don't know what to do. I am very sorry that I lied to you."

Miigwan: When Sunshine finished her story, I told her that we would talk things over and maybe we could find a way to help her. Collin and I discussed this serious situation when we returned to our camp. I explained to Collin that male residential groups, or extended families formed around male relatives, are the basis of the Ojibwe social system. They are united by marriage, outside the male's social group, in order to form a web of cooperating families in other locations who share resources, labor, knowledge, and other things necessary for survival of every individual. Such sharing is essential, which is why Sunshine could not survive as a lone person.

Collin suggested that we take her to the Sault and continue to hide her.

"No," I said, "We need to find a way for her to atone for the death in the Ojibwe tradition, which is called "covering the dead." To do this she needs to pay her former in-laws something of great value or they will seek revenge on her and her family."

It wasn't long before Collin saw a solution. He proposed that we take goods from our store which we could repay from our shares of the profits. That's a start, I offered, but she is a very proud and self-reliant woman and she would never be able to pay us back as Ojibwe tradition would require. Now I thought of an idea that made perfect sense. What if we take her back to the Sault and give her the goods to "cover the dead." She could live with my wife *Anangons* and me and help *Anangons* with her work, and I would not need to acquire a second wife as *Anangons* keeps insisting on.

I explained to Collin that among the Ojibwe, women are expected to do much work in support of the family and the band. There is often more work than one woman can reasonably accomplish so polygamy is not only accepted but often encouraged by previous wives who want help with their work. In this way the frequency of polygamist marriages is determined more by the ability of the husband to support a larger household than other considerations. I suggested to Collin that he could hire Sunshine in the store as a translator and assistant clerk and in that way, she could eventually pay off the value of the goods. Collin liked the idea but pointed out that Sunshine did not speak English, so she could not be a translator. I told him that she could teach him Ojibwe while he was teaching her English and he liked that idea.

The next day we made the proposal to Sunshine and she was overjoyed to accept. We packed up the following day and using Sunshine's hidden canoe we headed back to the Sault.

CHAPTER 4

Winter at Chequamegon Bay, Ojibwe Western Metropolis

Alex: On 26 of July, 1765, Josette, myself and our young ward *Shingabawassin* set out for our intended wintering grounds at Chequamegon Bay on the southwest coast of Lake Superior. It took several trips to carry our gear to the upper portage on Lake Superior where we loaded our thirty-foot canoe with all of the possessions needed to pass the dark, cold winter months. On our journey, we would be accompanied by four canoes containing the goods we planned to give in trade for the fur we hoped to acquire. These canoes were to be paddled by twelve men who I engaged for the trading season.

On the shore of the lake not far from our point of embarkation was a lakeside bluff called *Nodaway*, or Iroquois Point. Ojibwe oral tradition records that a battle was fought at this place perhaps seventy-five years ago between Iroquois raiders from the east whom the Ojibwe call *Nodaway* and local Ojibwe warriors.

We paused on our journey to visit the spot and to listen to the story of this battle told to us by *Shingabawassin* who heard it repeated many times by his grandfather, *Gitcho-jeedebun*. As in the case of many other societies which do not record the events of their histories by means of written texts, the Ojibwe depended upon a verbal means to remember those events, places, people, and the times that were important to their collective past. From an early age, Ojibwe children were taught to listen carefully to what was told to them by their elders and to remember this information and advice so it could be passed word-for-word from one generation to the next into their collective memories without error. This is called oral history and was the way the story of Iroquois Point was recorded. In telling us the story *Shingabawassin* used the first person or *daebaudjimowin* to distinguish between an historical event and a myth, which is in the realm of allegory.

He started by recalling the time long ago when the *Nodaway* had trapped all of the beaver in their own country and having no other means of acquiring trade goods from the whites began to raid their neighbor tribes to the north and west. Unlike the usual raiding practices of the northern tribes, which involved only small war parties, the *Nodaway* sent out huge numbers of warriors who attacked to steal fur and trade goods and to terrorize the people of the upper lakes country. *Shingabawassin* told the story in the first person as befitting an important historic event.

"I was living near this spot and we heard from our system of spies that a huge *Nodaway* war party of one hundred warriors was headed west toward Lake Superior. We left our village at the Sault to hide and keep watch from the bluffs besides the lake, and sure enough the *Nodaway* crossed the portage at the falls in great numbers and we sent out word for all of the Ojibwe warriors in the area to assemble near this place. That evening the *Nodaway* camped on this point which has since been named for them. Since the point was heavily forested, we could not actually see their camp until darkness fell, then we could see many campfires through the trees. We also heard much loud talking and yelling, which told us that the *Nodaway* were not afraid of being discovered or attacked."

"To plan our attack and kill the invaders, we needed more information about their camp. It was then that two of our most renowned spiritual men with their great power transformed themselves into beavers and were able to swim right up to the *Nodaway* camp. They soon returned to us, and again in human form reported that the enemy must have looted a cask of whiskey at the Sault since they were all laying around drunk. They had not even posted sentries, so we lost no time in creeping closer to the *Nodaway* camp and at the signal we ran among them killing them with clubs and knives. In a short time, the raiders were all dead and we had not lost a single warrior. We left their bodies to rot."

"For many years thereafter, bones, bleached white in the sun and gnawed by porcupines and mice, littered the point and to this day it is known to us as "the grave of the *Nodaway*." After that time, *Nodaway* raiders seldom dared to come back to the country of the Ojibwe."

At the conclusion of *Shingabawassin*'s narrative we continued down the lake camping that night at the mouth of the Shelldrake River, which abounds in all types of waterfowl. This is the territory of the Whitefish Point band led by *Kaygayosh*, or "gull," and of course his son *Shingabawassin* knew every square foot of his surroundings. Some of our canoe men decided to make a quick trip to a nearby lake hoping to shoot ducks for breakfast, but *Shingabawassin* warned them to be very careful. He told them that this body of water is called Manitou or "Spirit" Lake because it is in the domain of huge water serpents with short legs which are called *okadiginebeg*. It is said that Manitou Lake is connected to Lake Superior by an underwater tunnel so that the serpents can move from one body of water to the other. When the water in Manitou Lake is high the serpents are present but if they move into Lake Superior the water level is lower. After hearing this tale our intrepid duck hunters decided to eat dried fish for breakfast.

We proceeded down Lake Superior the next morning where we reached a very beautiful small round harbor which the French traders named Grand Marais. Recalling *Kaygayosh*'s warning about the cliffs on this stretch of the lake we paused to talk over the time it would take to pass the cliffs ahead and the prospects of good weather. After discussing the potential dangers with our canoe men, we decided we could pass this part of the coast in one long day if the weather is fair. Accordingly, we camped at Grand Marais and at sunrise pushed off into gentle swells. For the first few miles we saw only high sand banks broken by occasional small streams. By midday we began passing beautiful pink and a grey sandstone cliffs reaching two hundred feet above the water. Water seeping on the cliff faces left black lines that followed horizontal cracks and, from these, black fingers trailed down the rock beneath. Wave action at the water line in some places undercut the rock and in others eroded out arches and sea caves. We could all quickly see that if we were caught in a storm our fragile canoes would be forced against the cliff and smashed to pieces by the pounding waves. Fortunately, we eventually rounded a point and found ourselves in a bay created in the lee of a large island which sheltered the harbor, where we spent the night.

By the 19th of August we reached the mouth of the Ontonagon River. I wished to visit the lower reaches of the river where French explorers many years ago reported deposits of pure copper. A local Indian guide showed me a copper nugget that weighed about twenty pounds. After seeing several smaller masses of copper my interest was piqued by the possibility of establishing a copper-mining company to exploit this valuable mineral resource.

At a few miles further up the Ontonagon, we discovered the Indians of the Ontonagon band, who had a village at the mouth of the river. They had constructed a sturgeon weir by driving stakes into the bed of the river in order to make a barrier against further upstream migration of these enormous fish. An opening was left at the center of the stream so that sturgeon could continue upstream by passing through a narrow space. Indian fishermen stationed themselves on the weir above the opening so that they could spear any fish attempting to pass through. By this method they were able to secure a month's supply of food in a very few hours. On the shore above the weir, women and children were working smoking the sturgeon for future use. Some of these fish weighed in excess of one hundred pounds. I purchased a supply of dried sturgeon for the use of our party.

I should not neglect to mention that as we passed down the coast we met hunters from many small lakeshore bands whose villages were located at Grand Marais, Grand Island, Keweenaw Bay, Ontonagon, Bad River, Red Cliff and some interior bands such as Lac du Flambeau and Lac du Oreilles. During the late autumn season whitefish and lake trout were spawning on deep gravel shoals along the coast and could be taken in good numbers with gill nets. It was the practice of lakeshore bands each fall to catch, filet, and smoke dry as much fish as possible. This provided a food reserve for people and their dogs during the winter when the bands were on their traditional winter hunting grounds to the south in the Wisconsin River valley and further west. They then worked their way back north in the spring. As we passed in our canoes on our way west, we observed the fishers at work. The men were setting and hauling the nets and removing the catch, and women and older children were busy on shore processing fish and cleaning and repairing nets made of nettle and basswood fiber. To a stranger these scenes might seem disorganized but in fact were well planned by a traditional division of labor. All members of Ojibwe bands had specific jobs based on age and gender. When we passed these busy fishing camps, we could hear shouting, joking, and laughter back and forth among the workers who were obviously enjoying their communal work to the benefit of everyone.

As the season was now so advanced, I disbursed trade goods on credit to hunters of these groups, for which I will be repaid with furs as we return to the Sault early next summer.

Continuing our journey west along Lake Superior our brigade eventually reached Chequamegon Bay on the 1st of September, 1765. My priority was to build a suitable winter house, so after conferring with the local *ogamaw* or "chief," for an acceptable site, I directed some of my Canadian *engagées* to construct the building. They built a comfortable house in the French frontier style in six days. The outer walls were upright posts set into a wood sill, the spaces between the posts were plastered with mud on the outside to form a sturdy and weather-tight barrier against the rain and cold. Our house had plank floors and consisted of a common room in the front with a large fireplace for warmth and cooking. Two bedrooms in the back were separated by a hallway. There was also a loft bedroom over the back bedrooms which could be reached with a ladder. A pantry was built in one corner of the common room which had a cold storage cellar dug into the sand beneath the pantry floor. Shuttered window holes provided light and ventilation during the warm days. A toilet pit was located near the rear of the house which could be accessed by a door and raised walkway from the back of the house.

Lake Superior's Chequamegon Bay is the Ojibwe "metropolis" on the western end of the lake as the Sault is on the eastern end. The Ojibwe village is composed of about fifty lodges containing perhaps two hundred and fifty people. Since an equal number of Ojibwe followed us down the lake there are now nearly one hundred families seeking goods from me. The Ojibwe at Chequamegon are in poor shape since the new British trade policies put a great strain on the flow of goods to this remote area. The British limited the use of guns in the fur trade, as they feared that guns, shot and powder in Indian hands would be used against them in any future warfare. Unfortunately, this policy made it much harder for Indian hunters to feed and clothe their families. These Indians also lacked many other useful items such as warm blankets and woven cloth they traded from the French in the previous century. Under these circumstances, I was obliged to distribute goods in the amount of three thousand prime beaver skins. In addition, I sent a clerk with two loads of goods to winter with the Ojibwe band at Fond du Lac at the west end of the lake.

Because of their lack of access to trade goods, the Ojibwe people at Chequamegon Bay are dressed entirely in deer skin cloths but even considering their poverty they are very well groomed and proud of their appearance. The women divide their hair into two plats which are raised and fixed behind their heads. When vermilion is available, the women use it to heighten the color of their cheeks. The men paint their whole bodies and faces with either charcoal or white ocher, giving them a demonic appearance.

The Ojibwe at the west end of Lake Superior are at war with their neighbors who inhabit the forest edges and prairies to the west. These are the Dakota people who the French call the Sioux. They speak an entirely different language than the Ojibwe. For many years, the Ojibwe have been pushing west where they encounter Dakota hunters in the prairie-forest borderland hunting grounds, which are very rich in game and now claimed by both tribes. Over the years this conflict has intensified, with large opposing hunting parties stumbling upon each other in the contested zone. Warfare among the tribes of the eastern forest areas was typically very sporadic but as in all tribal warfare was brutal and terroristic. The goal of war was to kill as many of the enemy while taking as few casualties as possible. There were no non-combatants in tribal war so women and children were killed or taken prisoner as readily as men. Raiding parties would engage any enemy they happened to encounter. Raids were more likely to be made against known locations of enemy villages. Attacking groups tried to strike by surprise at first light and enter houses by stealth to kill the inhabitants with clubs and knives in order to not alert the other occupants of the village. Indian groups set out guards each night to try to prevent the raids. Warring groups also often sent war parties into the territories of the other tribe. Given this more constant threat Ojibwe villages, including those at Chequamegon Bay, were under constant states of alert during the summer and fall raiding seasons.

After settling into our new home, Josette and I turned our attention to acquiring as much food as we could to feed us through the long winter. During the fall, I hunted frequently while Josette and *Shingabawassin* traveled to the *Kakagon* marsh area near Bad River to barter for wild rice which is very abundant in that area. On the 15th of December, Chequamegon Bay completely froze over permitting me to return to my occupation of spearing lake trout and whitefish through the ice. By this method, I was often able to spear a hundred fish a day, each trout weighing twenty to fifty pounds and the whitefish four to six pounds apiece.

As we engaged in these activities and in our home each night, I schooled both Josette and *Shingabawassin* in the English language. I tried to make our language lessons fun. For example I would point to an object and we would see who could name the object correctly first in English then in French and Ojibwe. The winner would get some little prize from my pocket, usually a piece of hard candy. This game got somewhat complicated in Ojibwe since many things in use among whites did not have an Ojibwe counterpart. For example, chickens are not common in Ojibwe country. My students had fun inventing an Ojibwe name and in this way a chicken became *gagibad wabapinshi,* "a stupid white bird." After a time we invented our own new Ojibwe vocabulary. What fun we had speaking it among ourselves in public and enjoying the strange looks and smiles from Ojibwe speakers who overheard us.

In the process of giving lessons I improved on my own knowledge of Ojibwe and French. As might be expected from a young person, *Shingabawassin* was a very fast learner.

In early January an Ojibwe hunting party brought furs to my house and crowded in demanding rum in exchange. When I refused, they became unruly and threatened to pillage my house. I found myself abandoned by my hired men but managed to arm myself with a large pistol. I then threatened to shoot the first man who touched anything, and the tumult began to subside. Fortunately, this event ended without serious issue. I was much put out by the cowardly behavior of my hired men and when I berated them they promised not to let me down in the future.

Since rum was the heart of the problem I had my men dig a hole through the frozen soil and bury the rest of my supply. If the local Ojibwe believed that I had no spirits to give out, there would be no further problems.

CHAPTER 5

Shingabawassin Goes to War

On a sunny spring day Josette and I relaxed over a cup of tea before starting our day's activities.

"It's nice to have you home after being gone hunting for two weeks," Josette said smiling.

"It's nice to be home and we had very good success," I replied. "The snow in the woods was very crusty due to some warm weather and while we could move quickly on snowshoes and our dogs could run on the surface of the crust, the deer broke through and the broken crust cut their legs. In this way, we were able to overtake them and were able to kill a fair number. Of course, they are not in the best condition in the spring season."

"That's good news Alex," Josette said. "The deer meat will be a relief after so much fish. Things have been quiet here but there is a development we need to talk about."

"What's that?" I asked.

"Well you may not have noticed but *Shingabawassin* has become very attached to *Maidosagee*, "Loon's Foot or Big Foot," Josette said.

"Yes," I replied, "He seems like a very capable young man, I think he would make *Shingabawassin* a good friend."

"Yes, that's true," Josette replied, with a concerned expression. "Except that *Maidosagee* is also the war leader of the Chequamegon band and he is filling *Shingabawassin*'s head with stories about fighting the Dakota and the glory and adventures of war. I fear that *Shingabawassin* might go with him when he leads a war party west sometime soon."

I said that would be bad since I had promised his father *Kaygayosh* that I would see that no harm came to him. I reminded Josette that I was in a bad spot since in Ojibwe tradition I had no power to stop him if he decided to go.

"As you know, in Ojibwe society each person makes decisions for themselves and no other person, no elder, famous chief, or even a parent can order that person to do something they don't want to do," I said.

"I will however have a talk with him to see if he will choose to remain with us."

Later that same afternoon I found *Shingabawassin* busy repairing one of our thirty-foot canoes in a boat house shed we built on the beach. As I approached he greeted me in English.

"Hello father, how was your hunting trip?"

I said it was fine and then switched into Ojibwe for a serious conversation.

"Your white man talk is getting very good and your clan father will be very pleased. Josette tells me you are strong friends with *Maidosagee*."

"Yes, I admire him as do all the young warriors," he said.

"Josette also told me that you are thinking of following *Maidosagee* to fight the Dakota this summer," I said.

Shingabawassin paused as if taken aback but answered, "Our people have been fighting for generations, and I wish to be part of the tribe's history. I also want to help protect our people from the Dakota raiders."

"*Maidosagee* has told me that in our grandfather's time the French traders passed west of Lake Superior which was then occupied by the Dakota and brought them guns and trade goods for the first time. At that time, we Ojibwe were at peace with the Dakota and not only hunted beside them but occasionally even entered into marriage with them. Then in our father's time the peace was broken, and the Ojibwe began to attack the Dakota in order to drive them westward away from rich rice lakes and hunting grounds between *Ojibwe Kitchi Gami* and the Mississippi River. He has also told me that now in our time, we are extending our territory until we control all the land east of the Mississippi River. Many of our people live in villages in that country now and the Dakota continue to attack us."

"Yes, I can certainly understand your desire to share in the adventures like other young Ojibwe men your age," I said. "It occurs to me, however, that you are destined to help your people not by war but by peace. Someday soon you will be the *ogamaw* "chief" of the numerous Crane clan people of the Ojibwe. In that important role you will have the responsibility to stand between the Ojibwe and the Americans who will soon be the ones wanting to push the Ojibwe off their land."

"Yes father," he said. "But as an Ojibwe *ogamaw* would I not be better able to guide my people toward peace if I knew the horrors of war?"

"I agree. But if you go with *Maidosagee* and his warriors you may be killed and then everything would be lost," I said.

"I will think long and hard about your wise words, father," *Shingabawassin* said after a long pause.

By early April when the young leaves on the birch trees reached the size of a squirrel's ears and the season of making maple sugar passed with the end of freezing night temperatures, the Chequamegon village came to life. On the 20th of April a large group of women and children arrived by canoe reporting that their men had gone to hunt and to war with the Dakota. On the 15th of May, some of these men and others arrived in fifty canoes. Almost every canoe had a cargo of fur. Some of these furs were given to me in payment for goods I dispensed to these people the previous fall. In addition, I used all my remaining goods to buy surplus fur from them, which left me in possession of one hundred and fifty packs of beaver, at one hundred pounds each, as well as twenty-five packs of otter and martin. The Indians still had one hundred packs of beaver, which I did not have the goods to purchase. I hoped that Msr. Cadotte, my partner, and Collin could acquire some of these when the Indian brigade passed through the Sault on their way to trade at Fort Michilimackinac.

In addition to the furs, the warriors also brought tales of their recent battle with the Dakota. They said the Ojibwe, six hundred strong, had engaged a party of four hundred of the enemy Dakota. While I could scarcely credit these huge numbers, it was clear both parties were large. The warriors reported that after the battle in which thirty-five Ojibwe were killed that we retreated across a river and camped on the other side. Although we expected another battle in the morning the Dakota retreated leaving the unscalped bodies of the slain Ojibwe. They reported this was done as an insult since we expected that the scalps of our warriors would be hanging in the enemy village as a tribute to their bravery. But, by not scalping the dead they were showing contempt for all the Ojibwe people.

This account aroused the fighting spirit of the young men at Chequamegon and they prepared for war. Such preparation included acquiring needed weapons and ammunition, various charms and medicines to protect themselves from misfortune at the hands of the enemy and a small amount of food and clothing.

The following morning Josette told me that *Shingabawassin* had gone with the war party. A cold chill went up my spine as I feared for the life of this splendid young man whom I had come to love as a son. There was nothing we could do now but to wait for his return.

After twenty days had passed *Maidosagee* and his warriors appeared late in the day and I was among the women and children and older men who ran to the canoe landing to greet them. As Josette and I anxiously scanned the crowd without finding *Shingabawassin*, fear and immense sadness crept over us and Josette began to sob. I tried to comfort her, but I was also filled with grief. I found *Maidosagee* in the crowd and he told me what happened to *Shingabawassin*. He said the warriors traveled to *Lac Court Oreiles* where they were joined by a group of Ojibwe men from that place. They then traveled down the Chippewa River until they were near its junction with the Mississippi. Late that day their scouts encountered a large party of Dakota who appeared to be hunting in that game-rich area. Although the Dakota were vigilant they did not detect the presence of our war party and went into camp for the night posting guards and lit only very small cooking fires.

"We crept near their camp that night and were prepared to strike at first light," *Maidosagee* continued. "Since *Shingabawassin* was new to war I assigned him and two other boys to stay in the rear in order to protect our camp and if our warriors had to retreat to cover them from the advancing Dakota as they fell back. At first light, I gave the signal to attack and although the Dakota outnumbered us, we counted on surprise to give us an advantage. (Please see Map 2, page 41.)

"Unfortunately, our plan did not work. As we were quietly advancing and still at a distance from their camp, we were spotted by one of their guards who discharged his musket. As the shot rang out and the guards shouted a warning, we began to run forward."

"The Dakota hunters were all sleeping in the open with their guns and bows at their sides and they had only to spring up and face our charge. With the surprise gone and being outnumbered, the first Dakota barrage of shot and arrows broke our attack and we began to fall back and the Dakota to advance. I remember seeing *Shingabawassin* doing as he was instructed, standing his ground and firing at the advancing Dakota."

"Suddenly several Dakota appeared riding horses and began chasing our retreating warriors. *Shingabawassin*, who I assumed had apparently never seen a horse let alone a man riding one, stood still in shock as a Dakota warrior rode directly towards him. I believe that *Shingabawassin* was stupefied, frozen in place as the Dakota rode up to him and hit him with his war club. I saw him crumple to the ground, but I don't know if he was killed or taken prisoner. We had to retreat across the Chippewa River and from there returned home. One bit of hope I have for him is that if he had been captured, the Dakota generally don't torture or kill their prisoners and more often adopt them."

That very night I told Josette that I could not leave *Shingabawassin*'s fate unresolved and that I planned to go to the Dakota country and try to find out what happened to him. If he were alive, I would bring him home. My first thought was that I needed *Maidosagee* to go with me not only to take me to the scene of the fight but to help track the Dakota movements since *Shingabawassin* was struck down. After a day of rest in preparation, *Maidosagee* and I began our journey at dawn by retracing the route of the Ojibwe war party down the Chippewa River. Eventually we found and spent hours closely examining the scene of the battle and the abandoned Dakota camp. *Maidosagee* pointed out the spot where *Shingabawassin* was struck, and we found some traces of dried blood on the ground, but there was no sign of heavy bleeding. We concluded that *Shingabawassin* was not badly wounded and had been taken prisoner. We found the bodies of seven scalped Ojibwe warriors, so we spent a day preparing and disposing of the dead according to Ojibwe custom. We marked each grave with a wooden stake upon which was carved an upside down symbol of the dead person's clan. In this case most, but not all of the dead were Crane clan warriors. We prepared for this by bringing appropriate burial stakes with us.

Examining the Dakota camp, we concluded that the hunting party was made up of about eighty men and several women, perhaps more. They were accompanied by three horses which were used as pack animals, as well as many dogs. We learned that the Dakota left the camp soon after the battle and moved rapidly and carefully north along the Mississippi River. As they moved, they deployed scouts ahead, behind and on both flanks. Clearly, they expected to be pursued or perhaps feared encountering other Ojibwe war parties. They did not attempt to hide their trail, apparently in the belief that their numbers were large enough to defend themselves against attack.

We followed the Dakota at a safe distance as they continued north first crossing the St. Croix River, then the Rum River and finally the Mississippi. Then following the west bank of the Mississippi, they continued through flat prairie country to the Long Prairie River where they set up permanent camp. *Maidosagee* and I found a small brush-filled ravine from which we could observe the camp from a safe distance. I stared at the camp for hours through my collapsing telescope.

My first observation was that the Dakota were very much different than the Ojibwe in body form. Unlike the Ojibwe who as a rule were rather short and powerfully built, the Dakota tended to be tall and thin. The Ojibwe had round faces and heads; the Dakota had long narrow heads. The Dakotas were very fastidious in their appearance, clean, and their hair was well groomed. Looking through my glass, I could see that they were also a happy people as I could detect much laughing and joking. Their village was composed of several dozen teepees which were made of buffalo hide and decorated with painting. A large horse herd tended by boys grazed on the prairie not far from the village.

I saw no sign of *Shingabawassin* for two days, but on the morning of the third day as I scanned with my telescope, I discovered him sitting in the sun in front of one of the teepees. His head was bandaged and his complexion quite pale. At one point a woman, who appeared to be Ojibwe, emerged from the teepee with two small children and began talking to *Shingabawassin*. Since he was nodding his head as she was speaking, I assumed that she was speaking to him in the Ojibwe language. Sometime later a middle-aged Dakota man emerged and walked off but not before he

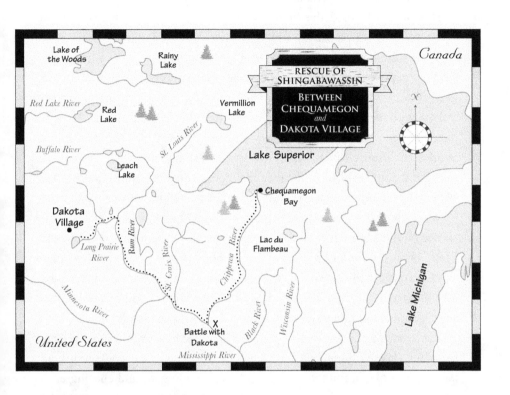

**Map 2: Rescue of Shingabawassin
Between Chequamegon and Dakota Village**

gave *Shingabawassin*'s outstretched legs a haphazard kick. Based upon this, we guessed that *Shingabawassin* was going to be treated as a slave rather than adopted as kin when he recovered.

Having established the layout of the camp and the whereabouts of *Shingabawassin*, *Maidosagee* and I discussed how we could possibly rescue him. We were both accustomed to moving about in the cover of forest and felt very exposed and uneasy in this wide-open country. We also knew that even if we somehow spirited *Shingabawassin* away from the camp the Dakota with their horses could easily ride us down in quick order. The only plan we could think of was to try to escape by water. If we could get him to the Long Prairie River, which was very close, and if we had a birchbark canoe, we could easily outdistance the clumsy dugout canoes that we had seen at the landing near the Dakota camp. But we didn't have a bark canoe.

We decided that *Maidosagee* would go to an Ojibwe village that we saw earlier on the Rum River and trade for a canoe. In the meantime, I would keep watch on the camp in case *Shingabawassin* was moved. Our plan was to rescue *Shingabawassin* from the teepee under the cover of darkness, take him to the landing, flee down river to the Mississippi, then down the Mississippi to the mouth of the Chippewa River, and then home.

The chances of me remaining hidden so close to a large Dakota village for many days without being discovered was very great considering all the children playing in the area, many dogs running around chasing each other, the presence of a large herd of grazing horses and the boys who attended them as well as women collecting fuel and plants. This almost guaranteed that someone would stumble across me before too long. My only hope was that I could remain still and totally quiet for long periods of time. Fortunately those were skills that I had learned as a hunter long ago.

Despite my ability to hide myself, I did have several close calls. At one point a woman collecting firewood almost stepped on me. I didn't panic and remained perfectly still as she moved on without discovering that she had come close enough to touch a dangerous enemy.

Six days later I lay sleeping under a pile of willow branches in the ravine when I was awakened by a rustling sound close to me. I slowly reached for my knife, but just as I touched the handle I felt a hand close over mine and a low voice said *anii* or "hello." *Maidosagee* had returned.

In a whispered conversation, we decided to execute our plan that very night. We waited until perhaps after midnight and with an approaching prairie thunderstorm rapidly blowing in, we crept up to the teepee where we knew that *Shingabawassin* was held. As I waited *Maidosagee* carefully and very quietly cut a slit in the rear of the teepee and disappeared inside, after a few minutes *Shingabawassin* stepped out through the same split and I quickly embraced him and started to hustle him toward the canoe landing which was two hundred yards from the village. I soon discovered that *Shingabawassin* was only stumbling along so I had to support him to get to the spot where *Maidosagee* stashed the birchbark canoe. We had not gone far when a huge lightning strike lit up the village like daytime and that was soon followed by a deafening thunderclap which seemed to shake the earth. Fortunately, all the Dakota were in their teepees because we were completely exposed. We had no choice but to keep moving in the pouring rain and soon found the bark canoe. We were shaking, with the cold and the fear of being discovered. My only positive thought was that the rain would wipe out our tracks.

Shingabawassin and I turned the canoe over and huddled under it while the rain pelted down. *Maidosagee* did not appear and I began to fear the worst. Finally, the storm passed, and we heard no alarm from the village. After what seemed like a very long time *Maidosagee* came to us. Quickly and soundlessly, we climbed in the canoe and paddled downstream as fast as we could go.

It was not long after dawn when we heard galloping horses in the distance and found shelter among dense shrubs growing on a small island. We were no sooner hidden than some Dakota horsemen appeared on each side of the river. They didn't know we had escaped by canoe, but it was clear that they were looking for a fresh trail that led in or out of the water. Fortunately, they were moving fast and didn't investigate the island. Given our precarious situation we had no choice but to spend the daylight hours in hiding and travel at night.

While we were waiting *Maidosagee* told us about his delay in leaving the teepee. He said that once he was in the teepee, he could make out the forms of five sleeping people; it was easy to discern the identity of the man and woman who were sleeping together and the small bodies of the children. The remaining form had to be *Shingabawassin*. *Maidosagee* put his hand over *Shingabawassin*'s mouth to shush him. He felt *Shingabawassin* stiffening and begin to struggle. *Maidosagee* quickly whispered in his ear *giwe* or "return home." *Shingabawassin* stopped struggling and seemed to recognize *Maidosagee*. Quickly and quietly he was directed to the slit and a second later was at my side. Just as *Maidosagee* was about to step through the slit to follow us, the tremendous lightning strike and thunderclap woke all of the family and one of the children started crying.

Thinking quickly, *Maidosagee* jumped into the bed just vacated by *Shingabawassin* and pulled the sleeping robe over his head and pretended to snore. The husband and wife exchanged a few quiet words and then the woman got up and comforted the crying child. Fortunately, no one noticed the cut in the teepee cover and in due time everyone was back to sleep. It was only then that *Maidosagee* was able to make his escape.

We hoped when *Shingabawassin* was missed in the morning that the Dakota would believe he had escaped on foot and since he was unsteady because of his wound he would not be far away.

During the daylight hours while we were hiding, I questioned *Shingabawassin* about his wound. He told me he was advancing toward the enemy when suddenly a huge beast came running right at him. Having never seen or heard about horses, he didn't understand if it was a human riding on an animal or a beast which was half animal and half human. He was frozen by intense fear and then he was struck on the head, unconscious. He later woke on a narrow bed made between two long poles that were being dragged by a horse. Since then his head sometimes ached painfully, his vision was a little blurry and his balance was not good. He also told us that he was getting better each day.

When darkness fell, we paddled our canoe to the middle of the river and soon after we entered the Mississippi. Now we moved very fast and within a few days recognized the mouth of the Chippewa, which we entered and followed north. We finally reached Chequamegon Bay and upon arriving home were hailed as heroes.

CHAPTER 6

Feast or Famine

By the month of March, the days were getting noticeably longer, and the daily temperature was rising so that everyone at Chequamegon Bay was looking forward to the end of the isolation of the long winter. Relief finally came on the 20th of April when the ice went out of the bay. On the 15th of May, fifty canoes appeared carrying families seeking reunion with relatives who they had not seen in many months. Among these were the canoes of hunters who had just returned from their winter trapping grounds. Their canoes were all heavily laden with the pelts of beaver and other furbearers. Since I had supplied these hunters with credits in the form of trade goods during the previous fall, their pelts were now given to us in repayment.

Sorting and baling this bounty occupied all my time even with the good help of *Shingabawassin* and my *engagées*. At the same time Josette began preparing our household for the trip back to the Sault. We were not prepared to leave Chequamegon until early June,1766. By the time we left Chequamegon, our four thirty-foot canoes were loaded to capacity, with each canoe carrying four tons of cargo. This fact alone was a measure of the fantastic wealth of furs to be reaped from the south shore of the *Ojibwe Kitchi Gami*. Although our bounty was great the Indian hunters who accompanied our little brigade eastward had much more fur, which I could not acquire since I'd already expended my entire store of trading goods. The Indian hunters were headed for Fort Michilimackinac, but I hoped that our people in the Sault would be able to acquire their pelts as they passed down the St. Mary's River Valley.

In the life of the Ojibwe, as well as all people who subsist themselves from the bounty of the land and water, food is either very plentiful or extremely scarce. When it is plentiful, the lack of adequate storage techniques to preserve food surpluses for a long period of time results in the development of a means to "store" surplus by giving the surplus to others. This custom represents a kind of "social storage." The gift of food implies that a recipient is obliged to reciprocate by giving food later when surpluses are theirs to distribute. Greed and stinginess are strongly condemned in Ojibwe society. I was often personally involved in this giving practice because I usually controlled surpluses of stored food and trade goods. I also had the ability to distribute these critical resources to large numbers of people.

This circumstance gave me much prestige on the one hand, but on the other I also felt a sort of social clumsiness since so many others were economically obligated to me in a society where independence was highly valued. In Ojibwe society the custom and etiquette of reciprocal giving and receiving under proper social and political circumstances had special protocols. These were the only reasons why the fur trade worked as it did, and why the Ojibwe and other hunting and gathering people were able to withstand the inevitable fluctuation in the supply of food they were able to obtain from nature. A practical example occurred just as we were about to leave Chequamegon to return to the Sault for the summer season.

Just a day before our departure a hunter from our La Pointe band discovered a bear den and included me among other men of our village to join in killing the beast. After the bear was dead, custom required that respect be shown to the spirit of the dead bear by consuming all its meat. All of those present at the kill were therefore invited to a feast. The bear was roasted over an open fire and distributed to the assembled guests which consisted of ten people, seven men and three women. It was expected that we would eat the entire bear, which must have weighed at least one hundred fifty pounds, at this one seating. My portion was not less than ten pounds but one man received as his share the head, breast, heart with all the surrounding fat as well as all four feet. These he consumed in less than two hours by which time I was not halfway through my much more meager portion. Even so I could not finish my meat and asked the Indians to help me, which they did cheerfully eating the remainder of my share as if their stomachs were completely empty. When we finished eating the bear, the feast was ended by a prayer of thanksgiving. Having eaten at least seven or eight pounds of meat I felt as if my stomach might burst, but my Indian friends showed no discomfort from the huge amount they consumed. As they say, "dogs get full but men never."

We passed the winter of 1766 to 1767 at the Sault and witnessed the opposite extreme of the hunter's diet, starvation. As in the case of many generations of Indian people living in and around the St. Mary's River Valley, as well as on the north rim of Lake Huron, and the entire land area between *Michigami* and *Ojibwe Kitchi Gami* people flocked to the falls of the St. Mary's to harvest the great concentration of whitefish which congregated at that place during the fall spawning season. Here whitefish could be reliably taken in huge numbers using hoop nets. These fish were processed by drying them on racks over open fires so that they could be preserved for use during the winter when other food became very scarce. As generations passed, the survival of all the Ojibwe people as well as many of their neighboring bands came to rely on their ability to obtain a large and steady supply of whitefish at the falls of the St. Mary's each late autumn.

When we reached the Sault that fall, we found the usual concentration of Indians, but their drying racks were devoid of fish. We were soon informed by various sources that the whitefish had not appeared that fall. This situation had not arisen in the memory of living people or even in the tribe's oral history. All the people at the Sault were starving, including our families. They had tried hunting deer and moose in the surrounding forests, but were not successful since the large concentration of Indians in the area had already exhausted all the game animals in the countryside around the village. The Ojibwe people believed that the Great Spirit was withholding the whitefish bounty because someone among their number had broken a taboo relating to the proper way to treat the spirits of the fish. For example, they might have fed the bones of whitefish to their dogs and thereby offended the fish spirits, who would have then withheld their bodies from human use. I heard rumors that whitefish might be caught along the northern shore of the *Ojibwe Kitchi Gami,* and so I sent several of my Canadian *engagées* to Agawa Bay to see if fish could be caught in those waters.

Regretfully, shortly before Christmas they all returned to the Sault driven by hunger. I also sent several men to follow Collin's and *Miigwan*'s blazed trail to the Straits of Mackinac to see if relief might be found in that quarter. Reaching the Straits of Mackinac they succeeded in catching several large trout and also obtained a few fish from some generous Indians. These fish saved our family from starvation, but we determined that we must seek a steadier supply of food, so we gathered our families and embarked in the company of some Indian families to Goulais Bay where we heard that whitefish might be available with gill nets and hard effort. As we paddled up the coast we passed several canoes of Indians fleeing famine. This disheartened us, but we had no real choice but to continue.

One morning as we began our day, paddling northward we saw an older Indian boy standing on the beach and landed to aid him. The young man's appearance was frightful, his skin had the gray-green pallor of the dead, his vision seemed unfocused and his body gave off a strange and highly offensive stench. He said he left his family in the bush where they were starving to try to find fish at the lake. We were all uneasy to have this young man in our company and it was not long before one of our Indian traveling companions spoke out on behalf of the group.

"*Zhigaag*, this boy has eaten human flesh," he said. "We think he has killed and eaten his family, which he pretends to have left behind. If this is true, he has become a *weendigo,* and he is very dangerous to us since once they have eaten human flesh, they have an insatiable desire to get more. We must find out the truth by retracing his trail."

I agreed to this request and four trackers set out to follow his back trail. On their return the next day they showed us a human skull and a hand that had been left roasting over a fire where the intestines taken from a body had been hung fresh in a tree to dry. When confronted with this evidence the young man admitted the charge of cannibalism, which he previously denied. He said his family consisted of his uncle and aunt as well as four young children, one of which was a boy of fifteen winters. They were all starving and the boy, and his cousin decided to kill and eat the others. First, they killed and ate the aunt and uncle, but when hunger pressed them again, they killed the young children who they subsisted upon for some time until the two boys set off for the lake shore. When hunger again overtook them the young man in our presence killed his cousin. The hand cooking on the fire belonged to this victim.

The next morning the father of the children in our party, fearing for the children's lives, killed the *weendigo* with a single blow of an axe from behind. We were relieved of the *weendigo* threat, but we still were starving. Fortunately, one of the Indian women led me to the top of a bare rock high on a mountain where grew a species of lichen that the Ojibwe call *waac*. We gathered a good amount of this plant and the woman, who considered *waac* a starvation food, boiled the lichen down into a substance with the consistency of egg white. The ensuing meal was bitter and disagreeable but also a welcome relief from hunger. The following morning passing Indians gave us as many fish as we were willing to accept, and we put ashore for a hearty breakfast.

Back in the Sault, hunger still hung over the land. In the home of *Miigwan* and *Anagons*, their daughter *Papakin*, now four winters old, awoke crying in her sleep and called out for her mother *ninmaamaa* "my mother." *Anagons* held her and said, "What is wrong *sagi* "dear?" *Papakin* replied *ninbakade maamaa* "I'm hungry, Mother."

"We are all hungry, but we have no food" *Anagons* replied.

"But *Maamaa* don't you remember when *nishoomis* "grandfather" *Manitou Maaiigun* "spirit wolf" named me? He said I would be a food finder for the people. I have had a strong dream about food, but I don't know what it means."

"All right *Papakin*, in the morning I will call your other *nishoomis*, *Wawatum* and he will help you find the meaning of your dream."

Early the next morning *Anagons* visited the *wigwam* of *Wawatum* which was close by and told him of little *Papakin*'s request. *Wawatum* told *Anagons* not to discount the dreams of children, because since children are not strongly influenced by worldly circumstances the Great Spirit often finds it easy to gain their attention as a way of communicating important messages. With that, *Wawatum* hurried to little *Papakin*'s bedside.

"*Anii ninoozhishe* 'Hello my granddaughter.' Your mother tells me you had a special dream," he said.

"Yes *nokomis*, but I don't understand."

"Well tell me your dream," he said.

In her simple words *Papakin* told him.

"In my dream I was in the big storehouse of Msr. Gabriel Francher and I saw many short, brown, fat men who stood in a line by the wall but said nothing. Somehow, however, I knew their bellies were full of food."

"All right child, get dressed and we will go visit my friend Msr. Francher," *Wawatum* said.

In short order they approached the Francher warehouse where they were greeted by Gabriel Francher himself. *Wawatum* briefly explained their predictament, and then they were invited inside. *Papakin* again seemed to be familiar with the place from her dream and led us to a small room off the main storage area. On entering the door she became excited.

"See, there are the fat men," she said in a high voice.

She pointed to a row of barrels along the wall.

"Yes" agreed *Wawatum*, "They do look like a line of little fat men. What do they contain, Gabriel?"

"Well for the past several years I have been diversifying my fur business by hiring Indians to catch whitefish for the new American market," Gabriel replied. "In order to wholesale the fish to that market, the fish have to be cleaned, salted, and packed into barrels for shipment. During the last few years a wholesale fish merchant on Mackinac Island has been buying my fish."

"Would you be willing to sell these fish to the company of Henry and Cadotte at the same price you get from the company on Mackinac Island?" *Wawatum* asked?

"Certainly." Francher replied. "And I wouldn't have to pay to ship them to Mackinac."

With this agreement the salted fish were soon in the hands of starving people. Although the people did not care for the salty taste, they soon learned to soak the salt from the fillets before cooking. The supply of fish was rationed out so that the whitefish windfall would last for the rest of the winter season. The partners of Henry and Cadotte believed that this investment would repay itself by the new business which would come from the goodwill and obligation of Indian trappers.

Stories of the special powers of little *Papapkin* soon spread throughout the upper Great Lakes region as the story of her dream and special power was told and retold in the *wigwam*s of the Ojibwe and Odawa people.

On a fine spring day as furs began to pile up in their warehouse, Alex decided it was time to check up on the retail store and warehouse operations. On the appointed day Alex, along with partner Jean-Bapiste Cadotte paid a visit to Collin and Sunshine at their establishment. Starting with an examination of the store ledger books, the two older men were pleased that the entries were not only well-maintained but showed a huge stockpile of fur, which came from both the winter returns for the trade goods credits but also from exchanges of goods for pelts made in the company store operation.

After examining the condition of the warehouse, they agreed that the pelts were mostly in prime condition and that they needed to be organized to be shipped to their partner in Montréal as soon as possible. After their inspection Msr. Cadotte told Collin that he just received a letter from a Paris furrier requesting a shipment of one hundred and fifty red fox furs which he would make into stoles. Collin and Sunshine were directed to unpack as many of the stored fur packs as necessary, to sort out the required number of fox pelts, and then to bundle them for shipment to France.

The next morning, Collin and Sunshine began to sort through pelts until they accumulated a large pile of the golden-red fox pelts next to their work area. What happened next was not only surprising to Collin but even in his later years, he could not explain to himself how it happened. He did remember that he and Sunshine were sorting the furs and passing the soft pelts between them and piling them on the floor at their feet.

Suddenly they found themselves naked in the pile of furs. They spoke no words but felt a simple desire which was entirely mutual. A shaft of light from a high window streamed down on the furs so they were encased in a soft, warm cocoon which Collin thought was like being enclosed in a summer sunset. The lurid smell of the wild fur only added to the erotic pleasure they found as they fell into each other's arms. They made love with a frantic intensity, which was an outpouring of the passion they secretly felt for each other since their first meeting.

Although Collin and Sunshine went on with their normal lives and work after their encounter in the furs, all their friends and even casual acquaintances in the Sault sensed a change in their commitment to each other and began to treat them as a couple.

There was however one part of their history of the relationship which had not been resolved and that was the promise that Collin and *Miigwan* made to help Sunshine atone for the accidental death of her husband by making the customary payment to his relatives in order to "cover the dead." Accordingly, the two men began to plan how to fulfill their promise during the coming summer. As a first step, *Miigwan* asked his father *Wawatum* to make inquiries among the Indians in the neighborhood to locate the village of Sunshine's husband's kin. With some help from Sunshine, *Wawatum* learned that the aggrieved family was part of the Black River band which had its summer village some miles east of Fort Michilimackinac on a small lake known as Black Lake. Soon after, Collin opened a trading account for Sunshine and he and *Miigwan* loaded their canoe with an assortment of items from the trade store merchandise. They then began their journey to pay the relatives of Sunshine's dead husband in order to "cover the dead" and therefore protect Sunshine and her relatives from any retaliation in the future.

Miigwan and Collin paddled to Point St. Ignace on the north shore of the Straits of Mackinac, where they camped to wait out a thunder storm, which with high winds and waves was rendering the straits very dangerous for canoe travel. In the meantime, the two travelers enjoyed the generous hospitality of a small village of people from the Mackinac Island band who were kin to *Wawatum* and they were pleased to host his son and his son's friend. When they learned that Collin was the relative of the famous trader *Zhigaag*, their pleasure of hosting the two men grew even more intense. That evening around the fire, *Miigwan* inquired about the present location of the Black River band as well as the names of its leaders and prominent men.

When the next day dawned clear and bright with only a gentle breeze, *Miigwan* and Collin pushed off and headed their canoe through the narrow passage between Round and Bois Blanc Islands and headed south for the mouth of the Black River at Cheboygan. The Black River is a fairly wide and slow-moving stream with high clay banks. The river flows out of Black Lake, which is widely known as a location from which sturgeon could be obtained in large numbers during the spring season as they come up the river to spawn. This place is also the location of the Black River band's summer village where *Miigwan* and Collin hoped to find relatives of Sunshine's dead husband.

The arrival of strangers at the village created a crowd of curious children and dogs as well a few adults who all swarmed to the village canoe landing to examine the arrivals and to learn of their intentions. The fact that they were paddling a heavily laden canoe whose cargo was covered by sheets of sailcloth increased the curiosity of the locals. After a short discussion with the headman in which *Miigwan* explained the purpose of their visit, the headman escorted the visitors through the mob to a *wigwam*. He explained to the occupants the reason for the strangers' visit.

Miigwan then asked if he and Collin could enter the *wigwam*, and when they were admitted and seated at the hearth both were quite uneasy since they did not know how the family would react to their message. But once they heard the reason for the visit, the dead man's father and two of his brothers made them welcome. The fact that these men were smeared with charcoal indicated they were still in mourning. After a time *Miigwan* explained how we met Sunshine and told her story of how she accidentally stabbed her husband, how she tried to stop the bleeding, how he died despite her attempt to save him. She said she fled to escape in fear of their revenge. He then told of her work at the trading store, and her wish to "cover the dead" to avoid a cycle of revenge killings.

The dead husband's relations responded that they all very much liked and respected Sunshine when she lived among them and knew that her husband sometimes beat her. But they were still very concerned that the husband's restless spirit was wandering about because he was unavenged. As everyone knows, an unavenged spirit is extremely dangerous to the living. *Miigwan* quickly agreed, and said we had come with gifts to allay their bad feelings and to satisfy the ghost of the departed. He then asked the family to accompany us to our canoe.

When we pulled the canvas cover off our cargo, a collective gasp escaped the onlookers. Not only were all the goods brand new, there were more of them than seemed possible. The two travelers unloaded blankets, ready-made shirts, spools of ribbon, bars of lead for shot, a cask of gunpowder, files, axes, drills and knives all made from steel, copper kettles, iron arrow points, bone combs, needles, and cotton fishing line.

Before handing the cargo over to the dead husband's father and brothers, *Miigwan* made a short oration in which he apologized to the dead husband's kin and expressed Sunshine's sorrow. He said that she hoped that these goods would ease his restless spirit and the family's taste for revenge upon her and her family. The dead man's father replied that the dead had now been "covered" and that no revenge would be sought. *Miigwan* and Collin were then treated to a feast and after thanking their hosts headed to the canoe landing.

The dead man's father then surprised them by asking if they wanted to take her boy as well. *Miigwan* asked "You mean Sunshine has a son?"

"No, but there is in our village, a boy of twelve winters name *Sassaba* whose parents drowned on the lake of the Huron," the father said. "The people of our village, of course, took care of the boy by providing him with food and shelter, but he became very attached to Sunshine and spent much of his time with her. When Sunshine disappeared, he was devastated, and the people feared that his spirit would leave his body, so he would either die or he would become possessed by bad spirits. So far neither has happened, but *Sassaba* has become very sad and aggressive with other boys, so he has no friends and spends most of his time alone."

After a quick whispered conversation, we agreed that we would take *Sassaba* back to Sunshine.

As a surprise, when we arrived at the Sault we asked *Sassaba* to wait outside of the trade store. After telling Sunshine about the trip to the Black Lake village Collin said, "We brought you back a present."

He opened the door and beckoned *Sassaba* to enter. Sunshine and *Sassaba* saw each other, cried out and rushed into each other's arms. Tears rolled down Sunshine's cheeks and she thanked us in a hushed voice, saying she thought she would never see her young friend again. We told *Sassaba* he would be living in *Miigwan*'s household, which was also where Sunshine lived. Sunshine gasped with joy.

CHAPTER 7

Troubles in the Fur Trade Business

It was the first warm day of spring, and the warm air over the cold water of the lake and river produced a wispy fog that was pushed by an almost imperceptible breeze as it crept steadily and silently over the land. Alex made his way through the fog to his appointment with his neighbor and partner Jean-Baptiste Cadotte, who answered his knock by opening the door a crack and at the same time releasing the aroma of coffee and freshly baked *beignets.*

"Come in, come in Alex," said Jean-Baptiste, "*Athanasius* has prepared a treat for us."

The two old friends were soon engaged in an animated discussion of village gossip until Alex finally spoke of concerns.

"Well Jean-Baptiste, I come this morning on an important matter which will require us to make some serious business decisions," he said. "Perhaps I can start by saying that although our fur company has made a great deal of money for all of our partners, it is apparent to me that the fur trade is losing its profitability for us and that these changes are the result of several causes."

Alex paused for a sip of coffee and a bite of his *beignet,* then continued.

"First of all, our exclusive license for the Lake Superior trade will soon expire, but even now it is evident that others are either already operating in our area or preparing to do so. First, there are independent, unlicensed traders, that is the *coureurs de bois* who have been engaged in the trade here for many years. Now there are also better organized small operations such as the Emalinger family in the Canadian Sault. But even the huge and powerful Hudson Bay Company sends trappers and traders into our territory. In fact, my brother *Miigwan* told me last week that he and some Ojibwe friends were scouting out a suitable winter post for next season near the mouth of the Michipicoten River on the north shore of the big lake. They happened to meet a party of Cree Indian trappers who had been sent south by the Hudson Bay Company into our territory. *Miigwan* informed them that they were trespassing but to little effect. As beaver becomes scarcer in other areas it seems evident that many trappers will be eager to acquire fur from our domain. This will be especially true when our exclusive rights expire."

"I know you have heard as I have, that a group of well-established and well-funded Montréal traders are discussing the possibility of forming a new partnership called the North West Company, which will not only work in the upper lakes country but also will pursue the trade west of Lake Superior in Canadian territory. The result of all this competition is that we will lose business to these new competitors."

"Yes," said Jean-Baptiste "I have heard of these developments and I share your concern."

"That's not all. Yesterday I spent some time with Collin going over our fur receipts for the last few years and we discovered a disturbing but perhaps predictable trend," Alex said.

"Our receipts of high value furs, that is beaver, otter, fisher, and martin, have shown a slow but steady decline, no doubt because trappers have been targeting these species for nearly one hundred years. As a result, the populations of these prime fur-bearing species are simply disappearing. Surprisingly, however, our volume of furs taken in trade over the same period remains quite steady. But the difference is made up by less valuable pelts, namely those of muskrat, racoon, bear, and wolf, along with some mink. We are also taking in a much-increased volume of deer hides as well as a few caribou hides. Currently therefore, the great majority of our inventory is now made up of low-value muskrat fur and deer hides, neither of which bring us enough returns to cover the cost of goods we give in trade.

"In other words, we are currently making little if any money in the fur business."

"*Mon Dieu!* What shall we do?" asked Jean-Baptiste, "This is terrible, Alex."

"Well, I have several ideas," Alex said. "First, we could follow the example of our friend Gabriel Francher and get into the American market by producing and marketing salted whitefish. Likewise, we could sharply increase our production of maple sugar which is another product that is highly desired by American consumers. Of course, these enterprises would require the development of new distribution and wholesale networks, areas of business in which we have very little experience."

An expression of despair settled over Jean-Baptiste's face.

"I have been thinking about two other possibilities," Alex said, "The first is that we could explore and perhaps expand our fur business north and west of Lake Superior into the British possessions. It is said that there is yet plenty of beaver in that quarter. I would be willing to cross over the height of land west of the big lake and explore new routes and trading possibilities in that region. Of course, working in that area would put us in direct competition with the Hudson Bay Company, which would no doubt rigorously resist our efforts."

"As an alternative I have another idea. We could investigate copper mining. I know from reading the old French explorers' accounts as well as from my own observations in the Ontonagon River country and on the Keweenaw Peninsula that boulders of pure copper as well as smaller copper nuggets are quite common on both the northern and southern shores at the western end of the big lake. Perhaps we could find investors among our old fur trade partners who would buy shares in a new copper-mining enterprise which we could operate."

"I would be willing to explore for possible mining sites and to acquire the equipment and skilled labor to do the mining," Alex said.

Jean-Baptiste looked into Alex eyes, smiled slightly, and then responded.

"I think our best bet would be in mining. I have also heard stories that gold and silver are sometimes found in the copper country. The alternative of expanding the range of our trapping enterprises north and west is very tempting, but the Hudson Bay Company men would not hesitate to meet our presence with gunfire, and I don't like the idea of sending our trappers into that danger."

"All right then," said Alex, "I will begin by organizing some exploring trips to assess our future mining possibilities."

It was risky, but I enjoyed exploring despite the potential hazards and decided to pursue the new territory immediately. As a first step of testing the feasibility of a copper-mining venture, I decided to visit the *Isle Maurepas* also called Michipicoten Island, which lies in the eastern part of Lake Superior off the mouth of the Michipicoten River. The river flows into the lake about one hundred miles northwest of the Sault. It is a high, rocky island seventeen miles long and five miles wide. Indians who have visited the area report it contains shiny rocks and rare stones.

I set off with two Indian friends by canoe to explore the island which we reached on a clear day under a bright blue sky in mid-May of 1766. Other than iron ore rock which makes up the south end of the island and a vein of copper ore on the south shore I found little else of mineral interest. From the south shore of Michipicoten Island, using my spyglass I could see another large island on the southern horizon perhaps about fifty miles away. My Indian companions said it is called the island of yellow sand. I was then eager to visit that place especially when my companions told me that the heavy yellow sand was so valuable that the island was guarded by enormous snakes which would repulse all visitors. I was so overcome with the notion that the heavy yellow sand must be gold that I became very determined to take the risk of visiting the island.

Sailing from Michipicoten early in the morning we reached the island of yellow sand late in the afternoon. I was eager to search for its mineral wealth, despite any guardian serpents, so I went ashore with a loaded gun. Entering the woods, I saw the tracks and bones of caribou and soon encountered a small herd. These beasts had apparently never seen humans before so did not run when they detected our presence. I killed three of the caribou at close range and we stayed three days exploring the island but found no mineral wealth nor heavy yellow sand, nor even gold. I did kill several caribou and we dried the meat for future use. Once fired upon, the caribou soon learned that we humans represented a great danger, and we could not again approach them so easily.

So far, my search for a mine site had yielded no hopeful results so I decided to return to the Sault before searching in other areas. While in the Sault I chanced to meet a young soldier, who mentioned to me that one of his officers at Fort Michilimackinac, a Lieutenant John Nordberg of the

60th Regiment, was well acquainted with the business of mining. I was determined to meet him so in the spring of 1768 I journeyed to the fort and met Lt. Nordberg, who agreed to accompany me on a trip in search of minerals. While at Michilimackinac, I also met Mr. Alexander Baxter, who recently arrived from England as a representative of a partnership of investors interested in working mines on Lake Superior. I shared my mineralogical knowledge and mineral specimens with Mr. Baxter and he inducted me into his mining partnership. We thus secured financial backing for a possible mining enterprise.

After we returned to the Sault for the winter season, we built a large barge to support our mining business as well as to lay the keel for a sloop of forty tons in a small sheltered bay at Point aux Pins, which is only three miles distant from the Sault on the north shore of the St. Mary's River above the rapids.

As I was discussing our mining venture with Mr. Baxter one day, he told me that he had been thinking about the economics of our proposed venture. Although I have long been focused on copper mining, Mr. Baxter said that the process of shipping smelted copper or raw copper ore to markets in the east or to Europe would be very costly. In fact, it would cost more than the worth of the copper product. He told me that since local minerals like copper and lead also contain silver as a minor component that our enterprise would be more profitable if we were to concentrate on producing silver. Toward this end, he sent several of the rock samples I had collected to England where they could be assayed.

In the meantime, we sent a crew of miners to the Ontonagon River Valley where they spent the winter tunneling into a clay deposit to follow a rock outcrop that contained a vein of copper. Although they encountered a number of large masses of copper they did not bother to shore up their shaft with timbers. So when the ground thawed in the spring the clay shaft caved in, representing a great loss of labor. We calculated the cost of re-digging the shaft which would now require timber shoring as well as an airshaft. This work would require more miners than we could supply with food in that remote country. Still, we sent out our sloop loaded with provisions in the spring of 1772 and were shocked when the boat returned with all the miners. We had no option now but to close out that part of our operation.

We still had hope of mining on Michipitcoten Island on the north shore of the big lake. We sent some miners to dig a shaft into a rock outcropping at a small harbor on the south shore of the island where I had observed a four-foot vein of copper. Our miners followed the vein by blasting their way through thirty feet of solid rock and followed the vein, which narrowed to four inches. We were disappointed and recalled our miners to the Sault. When the assays submitted by Mr. Baxter reached us from England, we learned that our sample of lead ore contained silver in proportion to forty ounces of silver to one ton of ore, while the copper ore sample contained even less silver.

Given the poor success of our mining operation, the expense of shipping copper, and the low proportion of silver found in the copper and lead ore, the English investors refused to continue to finance our operation. Disappointed, we were forced to conclude that under these conditions, mining could not be a profitable venture in the Lake Superior region. Accordingly, in 1774 Mr. Baxter sold the sloop and other effects of the company and paid off its debts.

Jean-Baptiste Cadotte and I, along with the other members of our fur-trading enterprise, were disheartened by the failure of our mining venture, but now I was more determined than ever to explore the idea of expanding our fur business to the Canadian territories north and west of *Ojibwe Kichi Gami*.

CHAPTER 8

Exploring the North West Frontier

During the long dark evenings before the ice was off the waterways, I began to plan my exploratory trip to the country north and west of Lake Superior which was generally referred to simply as the North West. Although I had never ventured into the region of Canada before, I had many conversations over the years with fellow traders, voyaguers, and Indians who knew the canoe routes from their travel in that vast area. They all agree that the hub of water travel for the entire North American continent is at Lake Winnipeg. From this body of water canoes can pass with only a few short portages to rivers flowing north and east to Hudson Bay, north to the Arctic Ocean, west across the Canadian prairies to the Rocky Mountains and the headwaters of the Columbia and Fraser rivers, which flow to the Pacific Ocean. Finally as I already knew, canoes could travel to the lakes and streams that fall into Lake Superior with connecting waterways to both the St. Lawrence and the Atlantic Ocean, as well as into the streams that are part of the Mississippi River watershed and ultimately flow to the Gulf of Mexico.

My own objectives for the trip were twofold, to gain first-hand knowledge of water routes into the extensive fur country south and west of Hudson Bay. Secondly, I wished to visit the Great Plains which had long been an interest of mine. Beyond simply satisfying my curiosity and seeing new places it was also a business venture to see if we, as Montréal traders, could enter the fur trade in a region already dominated by the English-chartered Hudson Bay Company. The company had long established trading facilities throughout central Canada and built a profitable trade relationship with the Ojibwe and Cree Indians who occupy that region.

My plan was to form up a canoe brigade consisting of twelve small and four large canoes which together would carry three thousand pounds of trade goods, but also most of the provisions we would need to supply ourselves and the fifty-two hired *voyaguers* who would paddle and portage our canoes. I also planned to ask Jean-Baptiste Cadotte and *Miigwan* to join me and to share leadership duties. One evening, as the time of our departure approached, Josette asked me when I planned to return to the Sault. I thought for a moment.

" I don't know exactly but I would guess we will be gone for almost fifteen months," I replied.

I could see her eyes widen and her cheeks beginning to color. Although Josette seldom expressed anger toward me her next words came back at me like a thunderclap.

"What! You plan to leave me for an entire year or more!" she said. "No way Alex, I'm going with you."

This was a response I expected, and I was ready with a reply. "I can't take you *cher*, it will be a very, very physically demanding and dangerous trip since the Hudson Bay traders will certainly oppose our presence in their territory."

"Don't tell me that. You know I can carry a hundred-pound piece over the steepest and rockiest portages. And I can paddle as long and as hard as any of the men you hire," she replied.

"Of course, I know that Josette, but I fear we will face violence and I don't want to expose you to the dangers of open warfare."

"You would face it, too, which is one of the reasons I want to go with you."

I could see the logic of her position and I knew I would feel the same way if I were in her place. It was an argument I could neither make nor win, so I reluctantly relented. Josette began to prepare for yet another of the adventures we would share as a devoted couple.

On a gray and cold morning on the 10th of June, 1775, our canoe brigade pushed off in a light rain from the landing on Lake Superior above the Sault rapids. Together our group consisted of sixteen canoes, fifty-two *voyageurs*, as well as Josette, *Miigwan*, Jean-Baptiste, and me.

Even though our canoes were heavily laden, we were fresh and made good time on a morning when the lake was unusually calm. Our routine was to paddle each day from shortly after dawn until early in the evening with smoke breaks every hour, while we drifted in our canoes. In the evening we would land and cook dinner which usually consisted of dried corn or rice cooked with salt pork. As an energy food we also packed a supply of *pemmican,* which Josette made by pouring melted fat over well-pounded dried meat and dried fruit. When the fat congealed the *pemmican* was cut into cubes and was ready to eat. This high-energy diet was occasionally supplemented with fresh meat, fish, or wild rice when these foods were available. After dinner we used the time until the sun set to repair our canoes, clothes, and equipment. When the weather was inclement, we constructed lean-tos to shelter from the rain or snow. On other occasions when caught in bad weather we slept under our overturned canoes, which were crowded but warm and dry.

Following this daily regimen, we reached the mouth of the *Pijitic* or Pic River on the north shore of Lake Superior on the 21st of June. (Please see Map 1: Alexander Henry's Travels in Canada, VI-VII) The next day we followed the shore west and passed the mouth of the *Kaministiquia* River. After fifty more miles of paddling we reached the Grand Portage on the 28th of June. The Grand Portage settlement is below the mouth of the Pigeon–Rainy River route over the height of land from the Great Lakes to rivers which flow in all directions from Lake Winnipeg. The Grand Portage site, which is on the lake shore at the beginning of the Pigeon River portage, was in later years developed by the North West Fur Company as a headquarters with a stockade and several substantial log buildings.

The Grand Portage is the entrance to a different world than that which lies to the south of Lake Superior. Here the forest is dominated by conifer trees, especially spruce and fir, and the landscape is built upon a surface of rock through which flow numerous clear streams and rivers, which connect many lakes both large and small. In many places, swamps and bogs make passing by foot nearly impossible. North of the big lake, caribou and moose are the dominant plant-eating animals, while deer and elk predominate in the forests to the south. The waterways of this region are perfect habitat for beaver, otter and mink while the forests are home to lynx, wolverine, fishers, and martin. Because of the very cold climate in which they live, all of the animals are protected by a dense undercoat of fur. The quality prime fur brings the highest price in the fur market.

At the time of our visit, Grand Portage was little more than a clearing with a canoe dock on the shore of Lake Superior. Even so the clearing was occupied by dozens of trappers and traders as well as the *wigwam*s of many local Ojibwe. Many canoes and their cargoes were scattered around the campground covered by canvas tarps resembling haystacks. Though our visit did not correspond with the height of the rendezvous season, the place was abuzz with activity. The visitors included both Hudson Bay and Montréal traders. We soon learned from casual comments we overheard that these men seemed hostile to each other. I asked *Miigwan* if he would circulate around the campfires to see what he could find out about the situation here and the canoe routes north which we planned to follow over the next many weeks. I also asked several of our *voyageuers* to learn what they could about the assembled men without divulging our own intentions.

Just after dark *Miigwan* joined Josette and me at our cooking fire with a serious expression. *Miigwan* reported in a very quiet voice that he overhead potentially dangerous news as the travelers spoke to one another. They spoke English freely in his presence not expecting he understood English and French since he was an Ojibwe in speech and dress. By eavesdropping he learned that many of the assembled men were employed by the Hudson Bay Company, and that most of the others were independent traders who often traded at York Factory. The factory is a large trading facility operated by the Hudson Bay Company on the west shore of Hudson Bay. Many of these travelers were headed to York Factory by the first part of the same route we planned to follow over the next few weeks as we traveled to Lake Winnipeg. *Miigwan* also reported that our arrival had not gone unnoticed and that the Hudson Bay men regarded us as intruders and competitors to their own interests. *Miigwan* said there was a large red-headed man among the Hudson Bay traders who was very threatening regarding our purpose in this region of the trade. I had expected this kind of hostile reception, so I renewed my warning to be very cautious when talking among ourselves concerning the purpose of our travels in the North West or the route we planned to take.

The next morning, the last day of June, we prepared to travel the Grand Portage which is a well-worn foot path bypassing the many rapids and falls on the lower Pigeon River. The portage, which the Ojibwe call *K-Tchi-onigaming* or "a great carrying place," over which we were required to carry our canoes and our baggage climbs over a steep notch in the surrounding hills, which the Ojibwe call "the ear of the person above." After eight and one-half miles we reached Fort Charlotte on the upper Pigeon River, seven hundred feet above the surface of Lake Superior. Passage up the Grand Portage required seven hours of severe and dangerous exertion. True to her word, Josette's work on the trail was equal to that of myself or any of my men. I must confess that due to pain in my back and shoulders it was more and more difficult each day for me to perform the hard labor required to travel the back country.

We finally attained Fort Charlotte, an uninhabited depot at the terminus of the Grand Portage on the upper Pigeon River. We reorganized our gear in order to prepare to ascend the Pigeon River. Our crew was exhausted and the next morning seemed to come too soon. We had a quick breakfast of parched corn sprinkled with sugar to make it palatable. We loaded and launched our canoes and proceeded to paddle up the Pigeon, but soon had to portage around a hundred-foot waterfall. The next portage, called Portage *aux Outards*, or "cranes," was three miles over a mountain to a chain of small lakes by which we crossed the divide between the Great Lakes and the Hudson Bay watersheds. On the 12th of June we reached a stream large enough to float our loaded canoes while our men walked beside them to push them through the water. (Please see Map 1, page VI.)

CHAPTER 9

Deadly Waters

O n the 13th of July, we entered *Rivière a la Pluie*, or the Rainy River, where we camped near an Ojibwe village of fifty *wigwam*s. The residents were surprised and pleased that we all spoke their language, and I purchased two canoes from them to replace two of ours that were worn by hard travel. I gave them goods on credit, but made the mistake of also giving them rum. They all became drunk, man, woman, and child. As a result, we took the precaution of leaving their camp in the night.

On the 20th of July we reached the Lake of the Woods where we found a village of one hundred Ojibwe from whom I obtained a supply of fish. They also prepared a giving ceremony for us. The headman formally welcomed us and showed us a pile of presents they had assembled in the middle of the village. We were informed that they were very poor and in great want of everything, especially rum which they called "milk." We received their presents and in return made a present pile for them containing one hundred forty pounds of gunpowder, two bags of shot, a number of small items and a keg of rum. As the men began to drink, the women brought twenty bags of rice. After the initial exchange, the women brought another hundred bags of rice, each containing nearly a bushel. The next morning the whole village was inebriated. The danger to us was only increased by the facility with which the Ojibwe women had participated in the evening's debauchery, freely consorting with my Canadian *voyageurs* and thereby producing a considerable number of very drunk and jealous husbands. As a consequence, we lost no time in leaving this place.

On the 5th of August we entered the Lake of the Woods. This lake is a treacherous body of water because it is swept by strong west winds and storms which blow in from the western prairies. Our *voyageurs* called the winds *La Vielle*, or the "old woman." These winds often create huge waves

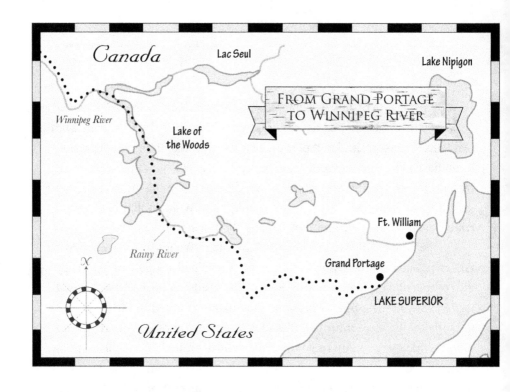

Map 3: From Grand Portage to Winnipeg River

CHARLES CLELAND

that make canoe travel on the lake both difficult and dangerous.

In early August we proceeded north up the lake where we overtook a small canoe brigade led by Peter Pond, a trader of some celebrity in the North West. A few years later, he became one of the founders of the North West Company, which dominated the fur trade in the Great Lakes region and beyond for many years.

The Lake of the Woods was studded with what seemed to us to be thousands of islands both large and small. To some degree the islands sheltered us from the "old woman" wind; however after we set out one morning we encountered a stiff gale and tragically lost four of our men and their canoe in the icy, swirling waters. Anyone who has traveled in a birch bark canoe knows they are light, fast and easy to maneuver but inherently unstable in high winds or rough seas. The men's canoe overturned quickly; we tried desperately to save them but they died quickly in the frigid water. We were acutely saddened when we pulled their bodies from the icy grip of the lake for burial. Shaken, we soon reached shelter on Buffalo Head Island. We knew similar accidents in the strong current could kill any one of us and sent silent prayers for the dead men.

As we made our way up the lake on the 7th of August, we were overtaken by a canoe brigade made up by trader Charles Patterson along with the famous explorers Joseph and Thomas Frobisher. We camped together that night and in the morning crossed a wide bay with the fleet of thirty canoes and about one hundred thirty men. Not surprisingly, we were soon very short of provisions.

At the north end of the lake we made our way through a maze of small islands and narrow passages until we found the Rat Portage. We passed over the portage on the 5th of September and entered the great *Winipegone* or Winnipeg River. After a time we crossed into the Pinawa River, which is but a branch of the Winnipeg and in turn flows into *Bonnet* or Hat Lake.

As we passed along the shore of *Bonnet* Lake which seemed to be a channel of the Winnipeg River, we passed a camp of several white men who were carefully watching our passage from the shore. *Miigwan* told us he recognized the red-headed man as the one who spoke against us at Grand Portage. He knew they were Hudson Bay men and very dangerous.

He had barely issued the warning when one of the men on the shore raised his gun and fired at us. I saw the smoke and flames issue from his gun and one second later I heard the gun discharge. I heard a thwack sound as the ball struck, and then I heard Josette scream. She was sitting in front of me in the canoe, and as I reached for her she fell back on a pile of rice bags. I could see that she was bleeding profusely from a wound in her upper chest, her clothing was already soaked with blood, and her face was ashen. Most of all I could see the fear and confusion in her eyes. As I tried to help her, I saw *Miigwan* pick up my long rifle and fire in the same motion. He shouldered his musket and fired again.

I could see that Josette was fading rapidly. Within a few minutes she ceased to breathe, and her bright and beautiful spirit left her body. Our canoe drifted as we sat in stunned silence. My heart was broken, tears flowed from my eyes. I was in a bubble of grief, feeling profound sadness and shock that did not leave me for many days. I could not imagine my path in life without Josette.

We eventually found a beautiful spot by the river for her final resting place, and I wiped her face clean of blood, kissed her one final time, and wrapped her in her blanket before we lowered her into the grave. I also placed some of her personal belongings with her which I knew she would want and need for her trip to the village of the dead. Before burying her, I also cut a lock of hair to have as a keepsake. As we returned to our canoes and pushed off, a deep sorrow washed over me. I knew I was leaving my love alone so far from our home and family in the Sault. All of us were keenly aware of the void her death left in each of our lives.

After we buried Josette, *Miigwan* said that we should go back to the camp of the murderers to make sure none of them escaped. I agreed and we did as he asked. The fire in the empty camp of the Hudson Bay men was still smoldering when we arrived and the bodies of two men were laying nearby. One of the dead was the red-haired man, who was shot in the temple which blew away the entire left side of his head. The other man had been hit in the thigh and was lying in a large pool blood. It was obvious he died from blood loss. We soon found tracks in the snow that indicated a third man fled into the woods. We followed his trail for about a mile when in the distance we saw a large clearing. On closer inspection the clearing proved to be a small partially frozen lake, the footprints we were following went out on the snow-covered ice but ended in a patch of dark, open water. There was no sign he emerged from the water and we were satisfied that the murderers had all paid for their treachery.

We had no choice but to continue. By the Winnipeg River, we reached our objective of Lake Winnipeg, the hub of the North America's canoe waterways. My plan was to exit the lake and to ascend the Saskatchewan River which flows west from the northwest corner of Lake Winnipeg.

As we proceeded up the lake a snowstorm blew in on the 21st of September and by the 25th all the smaller lakes in the area were frozen over with two feet of snow on the level ground. These conditions filled us with apprehension, because as far as we knew the country around us was uninhabited for hundreds of miles in any direction and if the rivers froze we would be stranded and quickly run out of food. This peril was not lost on our *voyageurs*, and we all paddled with urgency both day and night.

We gained the mouth of the Saskatchewan River on the 6th of October and on the 26th arrived at the Cumberland House after crossing the portage at Cedar Lake. Cumberland House was a trading establishment on Sturgeon Lake, which gave rise to the Saskatchewan River. The Cumberland House was built the year before by the renowned explore Samuel Hearn. Hearn was absent when we arrived. Cumberland House was however garrisoned by Highland Scots from the Orkney Islands, who were under the command of Matthew Caulking, a Hudson Bay trader. Although as Montréal traders we were unwelcome guests, we were treated with civility. After a restful stay at Cumberland House, I became more determined than ever to visit the Western prairies. (See Map 4.)

The other members of our brigade, which was formed as a result of our chance meeting on Lake of the Woods, all decided to pursue their original destinations. In early November we separated into several groups. Peter Pond and two hired men set out for Fort Dauphin. The Frobisher brothers and I elected to combine our efforts, and with forty hired men set off to *Amisk* or Beaver Lake which was but a short distance north of Cumberland House. We constructed a fort with a palisade which enclosed a house for me and the Frobishers, as well as four houses for the hired men and a large canoe scaffold. Our subsistence at Beaver Lake was entirely on fish which we caught through the ice. It was extremely cold that December, and on the 25th the thermometer sank to thirty-two below zero. On the 1st of January 1776, Joseph Frobisher and I left the Beaver Lake compound bound for Fort des Prairie and to explore the great western plains. The rivers and lakes were frozen and we traveled on snowshoes pulling our provisions on toboggans. The snow in some places was four feet deep on level ground. We were fitted out with woolen clothing and fur coats and hats, while at night we rolled up in buffalo robes which made sleeping possible. On the 4th of February we returned to Cumberland House, from which we departed on the 6th for the prairies.

CHAPTER 10

On the Frozen Prairie

O n the 5th of January, 1776, I left Cumberland House for my journey to Fort des Prairie, a trading establishment on the north branch of the Saskatchewan River. Two of my men accompanied me. I calculated that our journey would require twelve days, but after walking some miles the severe cold and deep snow was sapping our energy and therefore our food consumption was increasing at a far greater rate than I had imagined necessary. After a few days on the trail, we reviewed our provisions and concluded that our food supply would last for only about five more days. The men began to fear starvation, and I tried to reassure them by telling them that I would kill deer and elk whose tracks were abundant along the riverbank.

At this latitude and season, the sun did not rise until half past nine in the morning and set at half past two in the afternoon. However, it was never wholly dark in these climes since the northern lights and reflections off the snow provided sufficient light for travel. Fortunately, our path followed the riverbank so there was no danger of getting lost. We started walking each day at 3 a.m.

We had not gone far up the Saskatchewan when the harsh nature of the plains began to reveal itself. Tree growth along the waterway, such as it was, dwindled in both size and quantity to the point that we could scarcely find enough fuel to make a fire. Without a fire we could not make water to drink. Since the ice on the river was so thick that we could not cut through it with an axe the only way we could get water was to melt snow in our kettle. The river here had cut a two-hundred-foot channel below the surface of the surrounding frozen grass lands which extended to the banks of the river. The only thing visible on the flatlands were occasional groves of trees that grew along watercourses and, in the distance, often gave the appearance of

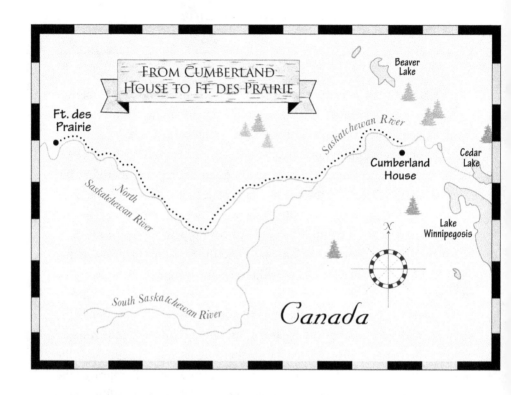

Map 4: From Cumberland House to Ft. Des Prairie

CHARLES CLELAND

islands on the flat prairies which otherwise extended uninterrupted to the horizon in every direction.

On the night of the 6th of January it was exceedingly cold, and I made my men sleep on each side of me under the same robe. This arrangement was particularly beneficial to me but added to the comfort of all. When we tried to rise in the morning, we found that a foot of snow had fallen, burying us and extinguishing our fire. We stayed under the robe until daybreak when with much difficulty we went abroad to search for more fuel and succeeded in finding suitable small sticks under the snow and started a new fire.

During the next two days, we decided that the deep snow and fierce winds, which blew up huge drifts made the use of our toboggans impractical and we were forced to abandon them and carry our provisions on our backs. By the 12th of January our provisions were gone, but I had taken precautions by hiding a large square of chocolate among my personal possessions. At the end of the day when we were losing our strength as well as our courage, I informed the men of my treasure and assured them it would keep us going for at least five days, by which time I predicted we would surely encounter some Indian hunters. I had the men fill our kettle with snow in order to make two gallons of water. To this I added a square of chocolate sufficient to color the water, and we all drank half a gallon of the warm liquid which refreshed us in body and spirit. We repeated this exercise the next morning, and then marched for six hours fighting both hunger and severe cold.

The faces of both of my men were expressionless, with blank stares which seemed to lack all focus. We all suffered from uncontrollable shivering. By the end of the day I was approached by my man we called Lobo who was ready to give up. He was a brute of a fellow, well-conditioned to the hard life in the back country. Yet he said he and his friend Maurice could not and would not continue forward since it was plain to them that they were going to die. He said dejectedly they might as well die right here as anywhere else.

In response I again prepared warm chocolate water, tried to ease their pain, and after drinking and having a smoke the men consented to continue. We marched well all day, but in the evening the men relapsed into despondency as the chocolate had been entirely consumed except for a single square. Since I was able to endure greater hardships than the men, I began to contemplate moving on without them in the morning.

In the morning I used the last square and we began our trek with wavering spirits. Our prospects were poor, and we were soon surrounded by a large pack of wolves that sometimes came very close to us. The wolves of the plains were not like their cousins in the Eastern forests, the Timberwolf. Here these creatures are called Lobos or Buffalo wolves, they are very large and powerful enough to be able to kill bison. Under the present conditions they were more menacing than might be expected, since as should be expected from a practiced predator they were able to sense and observe our weakened condition. We soon realized that they were following us in anticipation of an easy meal. In fact, we were also hungry predators and I had a gun. Wolf meat might save us. I fired several shots at them but missed each time. Fortunately, the sound of the gun frightened them sufficiently to keep them at bay. It occurred to us that they had never heard the loud noise made by a gun since at that time local Indians were mostly armed with bows and arrows.

Ironically, it was the wolves that saved us from certain starvation. Late one afternoon we came across the bones of an elk, which were the remains of a wolf kill. We gathered the bones and smashed them with rocks to obtain the energy-rich and delicious marrow that we boiled in our kettle and spent the night consuming. By morning hunger had lost its power over us and Maurice came to me and declared that "he and Lobo were now able to march on with renewed energy."

Another stroke of good fortune happened on the 25th of January when we found the carcass of an elk which had fallen through thin ice of the river before it froze solid some months earlier. Only the animal's antlers were visible above the ice. We chopped the carcass out of the ice and found the flesh well-preserved. We had enough food for the rest of our journey. I calculated we would reach our destination in only several more days.

On the 27th of January we were surprised and overjoyed to find prints in the snow of several of people on snowshoes. This was the first sign of human activity we had seen since leaving Cumberland House twenty-two days before. Although we remained alone on the endless prairie the prospect of survival was at hand and our spirits lifted to the point that we were again able to smile and joke. We arrived at Fort des Prairie late that afternoon. In all, our strenuous journey from Cumberland House had required ten days more travel than I originally estimated. We were fortunate to have survived.

CHAPTER 11

Among the Assiniboine of the North Plains

My men and I stumbled into Fort des Prairie after many days of cold and hunger and were highly gratified by the royal treatment we received from our friends at the fort who feasted us to as much tongue and marrow of the buffalo as we could eat. Fort des Prairies was very well provisioned, and in one storeroom I saw fifty tons of bison meat so fat that one could scarcely find any lean. Like others who find themselves close to starvation in the cold north country, my dreams were filled with craving for and then gorging on fat. I had no interest in lean meat.

I had come to see the prairies, and I had not yet satisfied my curiosity. After a few days, rest I was ready to venture on. The Indians who frequented the plains between the Saskatchewan River and the upper Missouri were called the Assiniboine. The Assiniboine were closely related in culture and language to the Dakota or Sioux and particularly the Yankton Sioux who inhabit the Great Plains south of the Missouri River in the Louisiana territory. These are some of the Dakota people who are fighting the Ojibwe for dominance west of Lake Superior. Like the Dakota, the Assiniboine are nomadic hunters of the bison upon which they depend for all of their necessities. Unlike the Dakota, the Assiniboine live a long way from the source of horses which come from Spanish Mexico. Since they have less access to horses, the Assiniboine usually travel on foot, and use their dogs as pack animals and to pull small travois. While at Fort des Prairies I met some Assiniboine women who had come to the fort to trade bison meat and skins. When these women were preparing to return to their village on the plains, I decided to ask them if I could travel with them and they readily agreed. On this adventure I was accompanied by my two Canadians, Lobo and Maurice, as well as William Holmes and Charles Patterson, both prominent North West traders.

We departed on the 5th of February at an early hour. The snow was four feet deep on level ground, so we were obliged to wear snowshoes. Although it is very difficult to travel great distances on snowshoes it is even harder to walk in deep snow without them. Walking in knee-deep snow is extremely strenuous and impossible in a deeper snow. The Indian women who led our party walked on long narrow snowshoes, which seemed better suited to travel in open country than the short and wide snowshoes which we brought from the Sault and were designed for use in the eastern forest. Even though they were tending their huge pack of dogs, the Indian women were more agile than we were. As a consequence, they were able to outpace me and my colleagues so that we had difficulty keeping up.

Our general course of travel lay to the south and west. For much of the way, it followed the banks of water courses which like other parts of the local rivers and streams had eroded channels cutting two hundred feet deep into the absolutely flat prairie lands. The only vegetation was along streams and in the few places with any surface water were low shrubs or stunted trees with a girth less than a man's wrist. We needed no axes to collect wood for fires since we could easily pull the shrubs out of the ground that was composed of loose sandy clay. Although the plains were mostly empty in all directions, here and there we could see small groves of trees which appeared in the distance as if they were islands in an empty ocean.

As evening approached, our guides led us to one of these groves so we could collect firewood and seek a bit of shelter from the incessant, howling prairie wind and blowing snow. On one such occasion we had just set up camp when we were joined in our small woods by a small herd of buffalo which had also sought shelter. The huge beasts continually bellowed and milled about pawing away the snow in order to expose underlying grass. We feared that they would overrun and trample our camp and us with it. Fortunately, the Indian dogs were able to hold the herd at bay. We shot two buffalo for meat and neither the sound of the guns, our fires, nor the dogs could drive the buffalo out of the shelter of the small grove and into the raging snowstorm beyond.

Our guides informed us that leaving the scant shelter of the small grove would put us in certain peril since the white-out blizzards driven by the fearsome prairie winds would cause us to become disoriented and die in the cold as many of their tribe had in such situations. While we waited several days for the storm to abate, we were joined in the grove by several Assiniboine men who arrived at our camp and revealed that they were messengers sent by the chief of the village where we were headed to invite us to be his special guests. The chief's name translated into English as "Great Road."

The next morning the skies cleared to a bright blue and the wind dropped leaving a landscape of bare patches of brown prairie grass and occasional deep snow drifts. Our party set out again in the same southwesterly direction following the messenger guides. In due course we arrived at Great Road's village, which was composed of about two hundred *teepees*, each having two to four families making a total population of about three thousand people. Assiniboine tents are like those of other plains tribes and made of buffalo skin stretched over long poles tied at the top and arranged in a circle at the base. The chief had arranged a *teepee* for us as his guests. During our stay of about four weeks we were attended by several waiting women who brought wood and water each morning. The water was for washing which seemed to be a religious compulsion among the Assiniboine. We were also attended to at all times by six soldiers or guards who accompanied us day and night. The duty of our soldiers was to keep curious villagers from bothering us. If people did not keep their distance after being warned they were beaten with sticks by the soldiers. I never saw this kind of behavior among Indians of the east. Our purpose among the Assinboine was to make friends and future fur-trading partners with the tribe if our business ventures might bring us to this part of Canada in the future.

The Assiniboine, as well as other plains Indian tribes, appeared to be much differently organized than the Ojibwe or other Indian people of the eastern forests with whom we were familiar. The chiefs seemed to have more authority, and the society was more complex. People belonged to a variety of subgroups specializing in such tasks as curing, feasting, and various other economic tasks. They seemed especially focused on defensive and offensive warfare. Our guards during the day, for example, belonged to a society which settled disputes and otherwise kept order in the village with the power to punish offenders, usually by destroying some of their property. Our guards at night were members of a warrior society which was responsible to protect the village from attack by neighboring tribes.

During the entire time we were guests in Great Road's village we never had to cook our own food since we were invited to feasts every evening by the chief or other prominent men. Each *teepee* was heated by a central fireplace which was vented at the peak of the *teepee*. This small fire was capable of heating the *teepee* to a very high temperature, in some cases causing men to strip off all their clothing. This seemed to offend neither themselves nor their guests.

On our arrival at the village one of the women borrowed my kettle, and as we were feasting in various tents during the course of our stay my kettle appeared in each place where it was used to boil buffalo tongues. This was almost always the main course. In our Assiniboine camp it became obvious that everything, including tools, weapons, fuel for the fires which was dried buffalo dung, clothing, housing, water containers, and sleeping robes were all made from buffalo parts. The buffalo supplied all resources for these people, and with abundance. For this reason, the plains Indians made poor fur trade partners since they were not in desperate need of anything we traders had to offer for fur. They didn't seem to need anything from us, except of course the use of my brass kettle. The kettle was much more convenient for boiling food than the traditional method of using a buffalo paunch filled with water, which was heated to boiling by adding small stones heated in the fire.

One morning during our stay, Great Road asked us to join him in a buffalo hunt since a small herd had been sighted near the village. The whole village, which included men, women and children, as well as thousands of dogs were included in the invitation.

At the appointed time we all walked to a small ravine where there were the remains of a corral in bad repair. We all set to work making repairs to the structure so that the buffalo could be herded down an entryway composed of a sort of alley made of four-foot high posts through which small branches were interwoven to make an entrance into a similarly constructed large corral. Once the structure was ready, several men dressed in buffalo skins and buffalo head dresses with horns approached the herd bellowing and moving in such a close imitation of the beast that I could scarcely determine which were bison and which were men. These decoys managed to entice the leaders of the herd to follow them as they retreated towards the corral. When it was full of buffalo a portable fence was moved into place behind them so that they could not retreat. Occasionally bison tried to crash the fence but were driven back by women shaking skins before their eyes. When the trap was closed the hunters began killing the bison with a shower of arrows. The slaughter continued until evening when the hunters returned to the village. The next morning the women brought the meat to the village on sledges drawn by dogs. The hearts and tongues of seventy-two bison were set aside for feasting, while the rest was either consumed as ordinary food or dried for trade at Fort des Prairie.

The entire village began feasting and dancing and, in the evening, Great Road appeared at our *teepee* with about twenty men and an equal number of women. These people seated themselves separately by gender and brought out musical instruments which the men began to play and the women sang. Their concert lasted about one hour and they then danced until midnight.

While in the Assiniboine village I met several slaves, who had been captured in the course of Assiniboine raids on other tribes. In interviewing these unfortunates, I learned much about other tribes in and around the northern plains.

To the east and to some extent to the north were the Cree, who in most respects were similar to the Ojibwe with whom they shared a mutually intelligible language. To the north of the plains and on the tundra lived many small bands of caribou hunters who spoke the Athabascan languages. Generations ago some of these bands moved to the American southwest where their descendants are known as the Apache and Navajo.

One of the female captives I met told me that she had been taken from the Pacific coast, west of the mountains, a region which is occupied by people who live in cedar plank houses and depend upon runs of salmon in the rivers for much of their food. Finally, the Assiniboine held another woman slave who told me she came from the south where she lived in a large pit house on the bank of a very large river. Her people grew corn, beans and squash and occasionally hunted bison on the high plains.

On the 19th of February, Great Road informed us he was leaving the next morning for Fort des Prairie and we decided to accompany him. At daybreak on the 20th, the entire camp was literally disassembled and we were soon ready to move. All of their possessions including the *teepees* had to be folded and loaded on travois. Our column was led by twenty-five soldiers who beat down the snow in the line of march so that the dogs driven by the women could walk more easily in the snow. All of the women had several loaded dogs and on average herded two to five. In all, more than five hundred dogs were carrying or drawing loads. Considering that each *teepee* weighed about two hundred pounds, the dogs pulling the travois were heavily laden. The dogs of the Assiniboine were quite large and muscular with the body build similar to a small wolf. Most are splotched with black, tan and brown color and had aggressive despositions. The women and their dogs were followed by the main body of men, carrying only their weapons, which were mostly bows and arrows although a few of the warriors had managed to acquire muzzle-loading muskets through trade with Europeans. The rear of our column was guarded by about forty men. The entire line of march exceeded three miles in length such that the front of the column could not be seen from the rear. That evening we came to a small wood that already contained an Assiniboine camp, which we joined. The meeting of friends and relatives was merry, with much feasting and dancing as well as the noise and commotion of women chasing dogs, and dogs of each camp waging war on the other. I slept very little that night.

The next morning the two groups united in the trip to the fort. Not far from the previous night's camp we came upon another island grove which was full of horses. The Assiniboine informed me that they belonged to another Assiniboine band, and it was their habit to leave the horse herds in an island grove to fend for themselves during the winter. They said that the horses would not go out of sight of the island and as a result could be easily recovered in spring.

We soon arrived back at the fort where I remained until the 22nd of March when my two hired men from Canada and I began our return to Beaver Lake. The trip back to Beaver Lake was without incident except that we were shadowed by a huge pack of wolves. We protected ourselves by building and tending large fires each night in order to keep the wolves at bay. Their howling, growling, and fighting in close proximity was disturbing, and we got little sleep in the open. On one occasion a foot of new snow came down during the night which not only buried us under our buffalo robes but also put out our fire. Fortunately the wolves were focused on assuring their own survival against the cold by burrowing under the snow or contending with their rivals within the pack.

After returning to my house on Beaver Lake on the 9th of April, I found the Frobisher brothers in residence and good health despite the fact that the only food was fish caught through the ice. As the spring weather returned, we welcomed increasingly more warmth and light. After observing many waterfowl flying north we surmised that the rivers and lakes to our north must be free of ice.

We decided to explore in that direction and especially the Churchill River with its connections to Hudson Bay to the northeast as well as access to the Athabasca River, which has its headwaters near the source of the Columbia and Fraser rivers. These in turn flow to the Pacific Ocean as well as north to Fort Chipewyan on Lake Athabasca, the termination of the Montreal-based fur trade. From Lake Athabasca, the Mackenzie River flowing to the Arctic Ocean can be reached by way of Great Slave Lake. This also provides water access to the upper reaches of the Yukon River drainage and to Fort Yukon and the Porcupine River. This gives access to the Mackenzie River Delta.

Joseph Frobisher and I met up with Thomas Frobisher and his men at the Churchill River where they had built a fort. In early June I began exploring the Churchill River country, which we continued to explore until the 24th when we determined to return to our fort on Beaver Lake where we arrived in late June. After a brief rest Joseph and I decided to return to Grand Portage, and we began this journey on the 4th of July, 1776.

CHAPTER 12

Strange News

The route of our return to Grand Portage is exactly that which we followed coming north late last season. Since the weather was now fair and with higher spring water in the rivers and lakes, we made much better time. Our route took us down Lake Winnipeg to the Winnipeg River, and I soon recognized the place where Josette was buried. We went to shore nearby, and I placed a bouquet of wildflowers on her grave. Joseph, Jean-Baptiste and I knelt in contemplation of her tragic death. I of course fell into a deep sadness as I thought of all the plans she and I made for the future together. My mind raced over the list we had recently talked about including starting a family, of putting an addition on our house in the Sault ,and especially plans to travel to see the huge waterfall on the Niagara River. The realization that these dreams were shattered was like a dagger in my heart. I was overcome by sadness in leaving her in this distant place with our dreams unfulfilled.

I was oblivious to my surroundings until I felt Joseph drawing me to my feet and guiding me to our canoe. We paddled on in silence past Bonnet Lake, and on down the Winnipeg to the Rat Portage and across into the Lake of The Woods. Unlike the last time we passed over this portage we actually saw several muskrats which preceded us in our north to south passage.

As we were making our way toward the south on the Lake of the Woods, we saw a camp of Ojibwe on one of the islands and decided to stop to see if we could trade for needed provisions.

One of the Ojibwe men spoke passable English which he chose to use in communications with us. I thought that strange since we all spoke better Ojibwe than he did English. He related a strange story that he heard at Grand Portage from which he had just returned. He said that an army of a strange nation had entered Montréal and had also taken Quebec City and killed all of the English. We were told that the invading army was made up of *Bostonnaise*, the name Indians use to refer to English colonists. I told Joseph and Jean-Baptiste that the Americans were apparently up to some mischief in Canada. The Indians also warned us that the *Bostonnaise* might appear in the North West and would likely be at Grand Portage when we arrived.

We continued south to the end of Rainy Lake where we encountered another Indian village of people who spoke the Cree dialect. They repeated the same strange tale we heard at the Lake of the Woods and the same warning that the *Bostonnaise* might already be at Grand Portage. These stories filled us with apprehension since we carried a load of very valuable furs which we did not want to have pillaged.

Eventually we reached Fort Charlotte at the head of the grand portage trail where we spent the night and prepared for the strenuous trip down the portage the next day. We decided to make the trip to Grand Portage in stages. First, we carried the canoe and left it about four miles down the portage trail, and then returned to Fort Charlotte for a load of provisions, furs, and personal items. In this way we walked down and back four times and then began again starting with our canoe. When we were still miles from Lake Superior, we could hear a muted roaring sound made by the distant but powerful waves breaking on the shore, and we reminded ourselves that travel on the big lake was a world of difference from lake travel on small interior lakes. We would soon be facing the power of what was surely one of the world's largest lakes, in every respect more like a sea than a lake. When we arrived at Grand Portage, we would need to exchange our small North canoes for large Montreal canoes for the journey on Lake Superior.

After several days of portaging heavy loads, we eventually transported all of our gear to Grand Portage. As before, the grounds near the canoe docks were full of camping traders and travelers, but there was no sign at all of the *Bostonnaise*. We spent a few days at Grand Portage resting our tired bodies and nursing our aches and pains from heavy labor and the occasional falls that occurred when walking over the rough portages. While at Grand Portage, I sold our small canoe and replaced it with a well-built thirty-foot canoe which was capable of taking the heavy swells on Lake Superior. I also employed eight Canadians to help paddle down the lake. There was no difficulty finding men to take this job since most of them were ultimately headed for Mackinac Island or Montréal to spend the winter with their families. At this season there were many canoes leaving from the Sault, Mackinac Island, and Fort Michilimackinac with cargoes destined for the St. Lawrence settlements. The Canadian *voyageurs* would have no difficulty finding employment.

We put our new canoe into the water on a beautiful late summer morning for our return to Sault Ste. Marie where we arrived without incident. We were greeted with hugs and kisses and backslapping, but it was not long before our friends and family discovered that Josette was not with us. I of course had to relate the story of her tragic death, which spread a cold shower of grief over the whole crowd of friends and loved ones.

I soon found myself at the door of our cold, dark house which I entered with trepidation. I quickly laid a fire, but the light and spreading warmth only intensified Josette's absence which was everywhere in the house. Our house evoked a horrible loneliness in me, but also a feeling of closeness with her which I had not experienced since the day she died in my arms. The only thing I could think to do was to retrieve the lock of hair I had preserved, and I tied a ribbon around it and nailed it over the mantle of our fireplace. Here I would see it every day, and it would help me keep her soft touches and kind voice in my mind in the lonely days to come.

It was not long until my neighbors and family came with food in order to express their own sadness and to offer help in my grief. They all told me stories about the kindness and heartfelt gestures Josette had bestowed upon them and related many stories of the good times and humorous adventures they had shared with her. Then they left me alone.

Not long after returning to the Sault, Jean-Baptiste, Joseph Frobisher, I and a friend of Jean-Baptiste who had a horse and wagon, decided to spend a Saturday afternoon cutting firewood for the coming winter. Jean-Baptiste knew of a place in the woods not far from town where many trees had blown down in a windstorm during the previous year. This downed wood was now quite dry and easy to harvest without the labor of having to fell large trees. After three or four hours of hard work, we loaded the wagon and distributed piles of wood to our respective homes. Jean-Baptiste, Joseph and I arrived at my house and I invited them in for a cup of tea. Our conversation turned to long-range plans, and I was surprised to hear that both Jean-Baptiste and Joseph were seriously thinking of permanently moving to and residing in Montréal. They each had their own reasons and I had to admit that the thought of spending a long dark winter in the Sault living in a lonely house did not appeal to me. In fact, there was something in the planned move that strongly perked my interest and seemed to complement the immense change of aging that I was forced to accept in my life. After so many years of facing the hardships of life in the north woods, I had endured all of the hard work and energy which was necessary just to survive. Now in my advanced years, having reached my fortieth birthday, I found my energy in such short supply I wondered if I could even carry on here. The thought of living in a modern city with all of its conveniences and the possibility of traveling abroad held much appeal to me. Before I knew the words were out of my mouth, I announced to my friends that I was thinking of making the same move.

Over the course of the next weeks, Jean-Baptiste and I gave thought to what to do with the Henry and Cadotte Fur Company. The business was not doing well financially but did have valuable assets and could possibly become profitable with some reorganization. For example, we agreed that the company retail store which was making money could expand its line of merchandise to appeal to American and Canadian residents who were beginning to settle in the Sault region in larger numbers each year. We also believed that although the fur trade had seen its heyday, that with careful management it would still make some money for decades to come. Likewise, the maple sugar, smoked fish, and Indian handicraft market were profitable at some level and worth pursuing as a business proposition. Jean-Baptiste and I decided to approach Collin and Sunshine and the *Wawatum* family to see if they were interested in taking over the company by buying out our shares over a period of time. We of course knew that all of the current principles in the company had substantial savings accounts with Montréal banks which would easily carry us through the transition as well as our retirements and beyond.

Several weeks later we called the extended *Wawatum* family together to ascertain their opinion as to our move and retirements. After studying this situation Jean-Baptiste and I prepared a written proposal for initial discussion. It was our opinion that Collin and Sunshine, who had recently married, had shown more than sufficient management skills and could take over the retail store operation as well as whatever fur trading might exist in the future. *Miigwan* and the other *Wawatum*s could together handle the field operations of acquiring furs from the Ojibwe as well as making maple sugar and salt fish and other products which might be wholesaled through the Mackinac Island merchants in the future. From time to time Jean-Baptiste and I would be available to confer with our partner Etienne Campion in Montréal concerning any problems, which might require our attention in terms of finance, trade goods supplies, or foreign marketing.

I started our meeting by reminding everyone that our fur enterprise had been amazingly profitable over the years, because of our hard work and that Jean-Baptiste and I thought that it could continue to be a good business for at least a few more years and with good management for many years into the future. But I then announced he and I were determined to retire. After a silence, Collin answered for the others in the room.

"We are all shocked to hear the news of your decisions and to hear of your retirement plans," he said. "And we are probably all feeling anxious about being able to discharge the new responsibilities suggested for us."

As he spoke however, I could tell that all our former partners were becoming optimistic as they realized new opportunities were presenting themselves. They also had confidence in their own abilities to deal with the new circumstances. This was especially true in the case of my nephew Collin, who in a few short years had transitioned from a recently discharged American soldier with few other skills into a successful fur trade clerk as well as a married man. With the proposed changes, Collin would become the leading merchant and first citizen in the entire eastern Lake Superior portion of the newly created Unites States of America.

EPILOGUE

Spiritual Home

During the next month Jean-Baptiste and his large family, Joseph Frobisher and I were able to buy passage on a sailing ship to take us and our baggage to the city of Buffalo on Lake Erie. In Buffalo, we hired a wagon to carry us on a short trip to Fort Niagara on Lake Ontario where we found a Montréal-bound ship. The ship carried us across Lake Ontario and up the St. Lawrence River to Montréal, where we disembarked. The next day I found several furnished rooms to let and had my goods delivered to 14 Rue Saint-Urbain, where I took up residence.

The very thought of leaving the north country where I lived half of my life and where I achieved my boyhood dream of becoming a fur trader on the wild northwest frontier of the Great Lakes raised great doubts in my mind about the wisdom of leaving. I missed the beauty of its crystal clear lakes, beautiful sunsets and endless forests. I especially missed the people with their musical and expressive languages, and interesting customs, the people who had been my family, friends, and neighbors in the north. Of course, I missed my Ojibwe family, my father *Wawatum*, my mother *Wabigonkwe* and especially my constant companion and beloved brother, *Miigwan*. I also sorely missed my little niece, *Papakin*, who it grieved me to think may be a fully grown woman the next time I might see her. I also missed the Sault itself, with all of its attachments to Josette and our life together. Beyond these personal bonds which I knew would endure time and place, is the country itself. I traveled the lands, managed to survive an Indian war, the attack of a mysterious giant bear, and nearly drowned or died of starvation on several occasions. I survived these challenges not just with my own determination to live but with the love, kindness, and skills of my adopted family.

I knew I could return to the Sault and the upper lakes in the future to visit after building a new life for myself in Montreal. I knew in my heart that the Sault and surrounding forests would always be my spiritual home.

Now I found myself a stranger in a strange city, and although the streets were bustling with activity as people went about their daily business, I was unknown to all and felt lonesome even while I moved with the crowds.

One beautiful spring morning when the air was crisp and cool, I decided to walk to the nearby square and have a cup of coffee at one of the outdoor cafés. I heard someone call out my name as I walked along. I scanned the nearby tables and to my surprise and utter astonishment I saw my old friend from Fort Michilimackinac, Ezekiel Solomon, enjoying the sunshine. I rushed toward him and clasped him in a bear hug.

"Oh Zek," I cried. "I thought you were dead. The last time I saw you, you were being led away from Fort Michilimackinac by an Odawa war party along with our trader friend Henry Boswick and several British officers. I thought you would be taken to their village and killed."

Zek looked at me earnestly.

"We were not sure of our destiny. As luck would have it, they decided to take us to Montréal in order to ransom us to the French. Here I am still very much alive. We have much to discuss. Will you join us?"

"Certainly," I replied. "I have just moved to Montréal from the Sault and I am starved for familiar faces."

Zek introduced me to his table mates. Among them was a small and very lively woman of middle age who had a sharp mind and a quick wit. Her name was Julia Calcutt Kittson, a widow of considerable fortune. I later asked Julia to join me for dinner, began meeting with her regularly, and found myself much taken with her. Julia seemed to enjoy my company as well. She loved to hear me relate my stories of life in the forests and with my Indian family, who she said she would very much like to meet one day.

As the months passed Julia and I found love for each other, and in the week of Christmas I asked her if she would have me for her husband. I was beyond gratified when she agreed and we were married by a magistrate on New Year's Day. In attendance beside Julia's friends and family members were two dozen of my fur trading friends from Michilimackinac, the Sault, and the North West Company. It was so good to be with these old comrades on such a special day. I decided to organize a club to make our interaction more regular. We called it the Beaver Club which was made up only of fur traders who plied the trade in the upper lakes region and in adjacent Canada. We all met for dinner regularly at a small inn in the city and never tired of hearing one another's adventures.

Yet even as a resident of a distant city, I found my thoughts returning again and again to the Sault and the family and friends I left behind. It was clear to me that distance and new scenes would not wipe away my attachment to the upper Great Lakes country and the strong feelings and concern I had for the people there when I learned of the onset of the War of 1812.

My concern for their lives rose when an unexpected letter arrived in Montréal on the 15th of September, 1814, by express canoe from Sault Ste. Marie. It was written by Michael Cadotte to William McKay and Alexander Henry.

Sept. 4, 1814

Greetings William and Alexander,

As I know that you both are financially and emotionally invested in the North West Company enterprise and to our establishment here in the Sault. I am writing to let you know about a recent disaster in this place.

As the result of the ongoing war between the Americans and the British on July 23, 1814, 150 Americans including regular Army, traders with Astors' American Fur Company, and a few Indians appeared here with the intention of destroying North West Company's assets and starving the British citizenry by plundering food stores.

In fact, this mob did burn two large and two small buildings owned by the company including warehouses which contained valuable goods. They also destroyed our canoe lock around the rapids, our sawmill and our schooner, the Perseverance, which was run over the rapids and then burned. They also burned whatever private property of those affiliated with the North West Company they could lay hands on.

I am sad to say that they burned your home to the ground, Alex. But on a good note, Sunshine and Collin as well as their three daughters escaped *to safety. I'm also glad to tell you that our agent at Fort William, at the west end of Lake Superior, managed to collect almost one million pounds sterling worth of fur and to send that cargo to the mouth of the French River on Lake Huron. These canoes were guarded by a party of our voyaguers against seizure by the Americans who now have several warships on the upper lakes. We have received word that that mission was successful so the furs should arrive in Montréal by way of the Ottawa River.*

I hope this letter finds you both safe and in good health.

Your obedient servant, Michael Cadotte,

P.S. Please give my best regards to my father.

I was of course crushed by the loss of the North West company infrastructure at the Sault and of the loss of my own home but very grateful that Collin and his family had escaped to safety. I felt deep foreboding of great change for my way of life and the people I cared most about.

The continuing War of 1812 brought great fear and apprehension among the people, both American and British settlers as well as the resident Ojibwe who made their homes on either side of the St Mary's River. This was in part because of new and often competing interests and policies in the domains of the newly formed United States of America as well as the British Empire. After 1763 British control in North America extended over all of the lands which had formerly been claimed by the French north of the Great Lakes. Both the American and British combatants in the Great Lakes area knew that the advantage to either side in any future conflict would surely go to the side which could attract the most Indian warriors to its cause.

The policy of both the British and the United States was to try to gain the loyalties of native tribes by giving huge numbers of gifts to members of the border tribes from their respective forts and settlements along the border. This policy was in large part driven by the paranoia of the U.S. Secretary of War John Calhoun and Michigan's Territorial Governor Lewis Cass. They realized as a result of the events of the War of 1812 as well as their personal participation in the war that the border country was a potential political powder keg. The native warriors were British partisans during the war and remained loyal to the British. Every Indian band in the border area contained sizable numbers of very experienced warriors.

Early in 1820 Secretary of War Calhoun authorized Michigan Territorial Governor Lewis Cass to organize an expedition to the south shore of Lake Superior. The main purpose of the expedition was to show the American flag in order to illustrate American dominion and to negotiate a treaty with local Indian tribes for land to build an American military post at the Sault. Expedition leaders also sought to explore the region's natural resources and especially to evaluate its mineral wealth. Henry Schoolcraft, a political protégé of Cass, was the chief chronicler of the expedition although detailed journals were also kept by another three members, who were responsible for recording specific observations.

The expedition also included a military escort of twenty-two soldiers of the United States Army, which was commanded by Lieutenant John S. Pierce. Lt. Pierce was the brother of the future U.S. president, Franklin Pierce. The expedition set out from Detroit on the 24th of May, 1820, stopped briefly at Fort Mackinac on Mackinac Island to pick up the military escort, and arrived at Sault Ste. Marie on the 15th of June. The events of the next few days were reported in detail by various members of the expedition, all from the point of view of the visiting men in charge.

Reaching the Sault, the tired travelers were invited to dine at the home of Collin Henry and his Ojibwe wife, Sunshine. By this time Henry was a prosperous fur trader and merchant in the Lake Superior region. Although Collin Henry was away on a business trip, his wife invited the tired travelers to her home. Madam Henry, as she was known by white settlers on the western frontier, was renowned as an accomplished hostess who served guests on fine English china and followed the latest manners and customs of the English gentry. She was also the daughter of *Waubojeeg*, or White Fisher, and a member of the Caribou clan, whose chiefs were the political leaders at the western end of Lake Superior. The Henrys had a large and well-appointed home on the bank of the St. Mary's River in the American village at the rapids. Sunshine, who had a keen mind for politics, was happy for the opportunity to talk with such distinguished guests.

Her household was a lively one, with three teenage daughters and an adopted Ojibwe son named *Sassaba,* who was in his late twenties. Although *Sassaba* was young, he was brave, impulsive, and already a noted warrior who distinguished himself as a British partisan in the war of 1812. Like all of the Ojibwe at the Sault, Sunshine and *Sassaba* had lost friends and relatives fighting the Americans. They were therefore not glad to see the Cass expedition along with its contingent of American soldiers appear in their community unannounced. Although Collin had been a soldier in the Continental Army of the United States in his youth, he was very proud of *Sassaba*, whose fighting skills and leadership of a large Ojibwe war band so impressed the British military that they promoted *Sassaba* to the rank of Brigadier General in the Kings Army. After the war, *Sassaba* returned home to the Sault with the red uniform coat, a silver gorget at his throat, and a handsome sword befitting his rank, as well as a military pension of a general officer in the British Army.

On the first day of the expedition's visit to the Sault, Governor Cass explained their mission to Sunshine and asked her to arrange a meeting with the local Ojibwe chiefs for the next day. Sunshine was glad to comply and sent out a message to the peace chief of the Crane clan, *Shingabawassin*, who would lead any negotiations with the Americans since he was the Ojibwe political leader who dealt with the Ojibwe tribe's foreign affairs. *Shingabawassin* spoke excellent English so he was able to speak with the Americans without the burden of having to communicate through at least one or more interpreters. Sunshine could understand English and French, but spoke only Ojibwe which was the language of her household. The expedition leaders were not aware of her stature with her people, as they assumed she was simply an Ojibwe wife and so not held in high regard by them.

Negotiations with the Americans took place on an open space along the river which was adjacent to the Ojibwe village made up of forty to fifty *wigwams* which sheltered about two hundred people. Schoolcraft estimated there were about fifty warriors in the Ojibwe village. The camp of the Americans was in the same area about five hundred yards downriver from the Ojibwe village.

The counsel opened on the 16th of June and resulted in a series of events that were consistently described in the journals of four expedition members and later reported widely by the American press.

Governor Cass opened the business by informing the Ojibwe that the United States wanted to buy a ten-acre parcel of land along the river on which to build and garrison a fort so that the United States could control water traffic into Lake Superior. The Ojibwe were dubious about a permanent American military presence in their location, but became outraged when Cass announced that the U.S. did not actually have to buy the land since it was already owned by the government. He explained that the U.S. had made a treaty with a confederacy of tribes in the Ohio country called the Treaty of Greenville in 1795. By the terms of that treaty, the Ohio tribes agreed that all the land, previously ceded to either the French or British, would now belong to the United States. Under those circumstances since the French had a fort at the Sault many years before, the United States now claimed to own the ground the fort was built on near the rapids.

"Even so," Cass said, "The Great Father in Washington, the President of the United States, would be willing to repurchase the land."

Shingabawassin was incensed by Cass's words, and replied that the Lake Superior Ojibwe knew nothing of such a treaty made twenty-five years ago in another place by people that did not occupy the land that Cass wanted. Cass told the assembled Ojibwe that the U.S. would occupy the land they needed "whether the Ojibwe renewed the lease or not." The war chief *Sassaba* was the last chief to speak and did so while wearing his scarlet uniform coat of a British general officer. *Sassaba* was also the war chief of the Crane clan people at the eastern end of Lake Superior. He angrily kicked away a present of tobacco which Cass had dismissively thrown on the ground before them and then thrust his spear into the ground before stalking off.

As the conference was breaking up, Cass noticed that the British national flag known as the "Union Jack" had been raised on a pole over the Ojibwe village in clear sight of the treaty grounds. Cass was outraged at this show of defiance, which he saw as an insult to the sovereignty of the United States. Cass immediately called the expedition to arms and with only an interpreter proceeded to the village flagpole and tore down the offending flag. Through his interpreter he told the people of the Ojibwe village "that if they continue such disloyal behavior, he would set a strong foot upon their necks and crush them to the earth."

Tension continued escalating. Both camps prepared to attack and the river was soon filled with canoes containing women and children fleeing to the safety of the Canadian shore. In the armed standoff that ensued about fifty Ojibwe warriors armed with outdated smooth bore muskets and bows and arrows faced sixty-six well-armed and disciplined Americans, including professional soldiers.

It was clear that a battle would prove a disaster for the Ojibwe who were both out-numbered and out-gunned. Sunshine appeared and quickly understood the impending disaster awaiting her kinsmen. Wisely she asked the other chiefs to "be quick and suppress the follies of her son, *Sassaba*." Agreeing, the chief asked *Shingabawassin* to find and help calm *Sassaba*. He was successful and narrowly diverted a war party on its way to attack the Americans.

The pending battle was avoided, a battle which would have certainly resulted in the deaths of many of the assembled Ojibwe warriors.

The discussion of the desired land cession was reconvened the next day, and the ten-acre parcel the Americans wanted was ceded by the Ojibwe, even though the parcel demanded by the U.S. contained the site of the traditional burial mound of the Sault band of Ojibwe.

When word of the treaty and the events involving Cass and the British flag reached the American press by way of the several male members of his expedition, Cass was portrayed as a great American hero who not only avenged an insult to the nation but also avoided an Indian war on the northern frontier by his brave actions. This was typical of major events of the time, written and interpreted by the dominant American leaders from their point of view with little understanding of Ojibwe life, roles and customs. The Ojibwe involved in the near-fatal confrontation had a much different view of what had transpired in the critical moments leading up to the near deadly battle.

If the truth had been known it was a brave and clear-thinking Ojibwe woman, Sunshine, the mother of the Sault war chief *Sassaba* and Ojibwe wife of fur trader Collin Henry, who had saved the day.

When word of this incident reached Alexander Henry in Montréal, he was having coffee with a group of former fur traders from the North West. He told his assembled friends that he had known both *Shingabawassin* and *Sassaba* since they were boys, and that they had very different personalities. He related how *Sassaba* lost his parents at the age of four and because of the trauma of separation he suffered, he had been known to be a troublesome and aggressive child, prone to picking fights. Even though his adoptive mother Sunshine had tried to raise him as a thoughtful and caring young man, the experience of losing both of his parents as well as almost losing Sunshine had regretfully left him with anti-social inclinations. *Shingabawassin*, on the other hand, was always a sensitive, intelligent, and thoughtful young man who was carefully raised by his father to use his talents to promote peaceful solutions to problems.

"My wife Josette and I had once been *Shingabawassin*'s teachers," Alex said. "We taught him to speak English and knew of his desire to be a seeker of peace. I remember telling him that although the Ojibwe had to fight the Dakota to protect their land and hunting rights, that the Americans quest for land would be a much bigger and more important problem for the Ojibwe in the future. It would seem that his diplomacy during the recent problems with the Americans at the Sault showed that he has taken my opinion to heart."

Any honest analysis of the events at the Sault in June of 1820 must conclude that it was Sunshine who stopped an impending war on the northern border that surely would have been a disaster for the Ojibwe and probably for the Americans as well. Irrespective of what the Americans thought about Lewis Cass and the story of his bravery, the problem was actually resolved by Sunshine, a wise and brave Ojibwe woman who did not receive public notice for her bravery and good sense. Accounts at the time gave her little credit for her role, but in later years several members of the Cass expedition acknowledged Sunshine's important part, and even Henry Schoolcraft wrote of her contribution in stopping an Indian war between the Americans and the Ojibwe people on the border with British

Canada.

Schoolcraft took an interest in the life of Sunshine after he met her daughter, Jane, during the expedition to the Sault and began a romantic interest. He and Jane eventually married, and he learned much about her family and the Ojibwe culture. He belatedly publicly credited Sunshine's role in the events of the 15th of June, 1820.

Alexander Henry remained true to his people until he died in 1824. It is difficult to comprehend the breadth and scope of this brave man who lived his life in quest of a youthful vision. That vision not only fed his adventurous spirit, but provided a path to the future for many pioneers who followed him into the northern wilderness.

In the wilderness, Alexander Henry found kinship with the native people he so admired, and the love of a woman who matched his own sense of adventure. Alexander Henry brought to the frontier a sense of bravery, faithfulness, and determination inspiring to all whose lives he touched.

The Real-Life People and Stories Behind the Characters

Anishnabe

This term is used by the Ojibwe, Odawa, and Anishnabeg to refer to themselves as a people who speak dialects of the same language and share parts of a common mythological history as well as many cultural practices. The Potawatomi are also known as "people of the three fires." In the broadest sense Anishnabe is sometimes used synonymously with "an Indian of Algonquian descent." More specifically it implies that the *Anishnabeg* (plural) are the true human beings of a separate creation.

Alexander Henry

This book is based upon the real-life travels of the historic figure and adventurer Alexander Henry. Henry was a noted fur trader in both the Lake Michigan and Lake Superior region during the eighteenth century, with intimate knowledge of life and culture among native people. Henry was admired for his bravery and grit when facing the hardships of frontier life. He was a canoe traveler on the river highways and lakes of the region and also walked hundreds of miles through the immense forests and featureless prairies in all seasons. He charted the geography of much of central North America for generations of Americans and Canadians who today figuratively follow his snowshoe tracks and the wake of his canoes.

Henry provides one of the very few first-hand descriptions of Ojibwe, Odawa, Cree, and Assiniboine cultures at the time when native people were still living from the land, speaking their own languages, and practicing their age-old cultural traditions. As an adopted member of an Ojibwe family, Henry knew and described their lives in the mid-eighteenth century from a personal perspective, which is rarely available to native people or modern ethnographers.

After retiring to Montréal, Alexander Henry had a very active life that included keeping up with many of his former trading friends and partners as well as his life with his new bride, Julia Kittson. They raised six children of their own together as well as two Kittson children. Alex was active in Montréal society and served at various times as a captain in the Montréal militia and as a Justice of the Peace. He also wrote a memoir titled *"Travels and Adventures in Canada and the Indian Territories between the years 1760 and 1776."* This work which was was published in New York in 1809 was used as the basis for this novel. Although retired, Henry remained connected to the fur trade by association with his partners in the North West Company. He also stayed in touch with his old friend and fur trade merchant at Fort Michilimackinac, John Askin, and others including John Jacob Astor of the American Fur Company.

While living in Montréal, Henry made several trips to Europe and was invited to address the Royal Society in London about his travels on the northwestern Great Lakes frontier. He also was invited to visit Versailles, where he had an audience with the queen of France, Marie Antoinette. Even though Henry was an accomplished and sophisticated raconteur, he found the queen and her court's reception to be condescending.

Henry returned to Montréal and died at age eighty-five in April 1824. He was celebrated as a pioneer fur trader, merchant, and historical author. As he was renowned for his extraordinary adventures and exploration, he was truly a witness to important Canadian and American history.

Bostonnaise

Alexander Henry first heard the term *Bostonnaise* as he traveled south returning from his exploration in the western prairies and in route to Grand Portage. On several occasions along the way Indians reported that "an Army of a strange nation composed of *Bostonnaise* had entered both Québec and Montréal and had killed British." This mysterious and troubling rumor was more truth than fiction since during the American Revolution, General George Washington sent a militia force composed of New England troops north to thwart the British in Canada. The British were trying to capture the Hudson River Valley in order to cut the colonies into two parts. So the "strange nation" was the newly formed United States of America and the militia was composed of New England colonists which Indians refer to as *Bostonnaise*, or American colonists. This militia indeed captured both Montréal and Québec and killed many of the defenders who were members of the British Army and local militia.

Fur trade competition

The international trade in beaver pelts and other fur-bearing species, was an extremely profitable commercial enterprise that featured fierce competition between individual traders, trading consortiums, trading companies and Euro-American nations. At its peak, fur trading was among the primary economic ventures in North America. In Alexander Henry's time, the North West Company founded in 1787 was among the largest and operated out of Montréal, Chequamegon Bay and Grand Portage and other locations. The Hudson Bay Company chartered in London in 1670 was a major competitor of the North West company. Smaller companies also were competitors, including the XYZ company, the South West Company and the Mackinac Company founded in 1783. The lucrative fur trading business also attracted individual traders such as John Askin, who operated out of Fort Michilimackinac, and the Charles Ermatinger family, which traded out of the Canadian Sault.

The small and large competitors continued to dominate geographical territories until the fur trading business began to slow during the second quarter of the nineteenth century. Demand for high-quality fur including beaver, martin, and otter was declining in Europe and America. After 1808 when the American Fur Company of John Jacob Astor began operating out of Mackinac Island, the Charles Ermatinger company dominated the Canadian side of the US-Canadian border. The Hudson Bay Company and the North West Company competed north of the border in British Canada. In 1816 the American Fur Company acquired the assets of the North West Company and took nearly complete control of the trade. The Henry and Cadotte Company mentioned in the text is fictional, although both men were real and well-established fur traders.

Josette

It was customary for fur traders and their *Métis engagées* to have both a country wife, usually of Indian or *Métis* descent, as well as a town wife, usually Caucasian or *Métis*. The traders lived and traveled with their country wives during the summer season and stayed with their town wives during the winter. The children of the country wives were usually sent east or to Europe for education and often returned to the fur trade as clerks. Alexander Henry had a country wife, but her name is unknown, his town wife was Julia Kittson. Josette is a fictional character, but she represents the crucial role of country wives who supported the fur traders and preformed many important tasks necessary for the business to prosper.

Métis

During the time when the French controlled the Great Lakes, country people who shared Indian and French parentage were known as *Métis*. *Métis* often formed their own communities, lived in western-style houses, wore a combination of Indian and French dress, generally spoke French and at least one Indian language. They were predominantly Catholic. Many *Métis* were engaged in the fur trade as voyageurs who paddled canoes and carried baggage over portages. They were also often involved in the acquisition of furs from native people to whom they were frequently related by blood or marriage. In that role they often acted as middlemen and advisers to native people in their relations with French and English settlers and fur traders. *Métis* were crucial to the operation of the Great Lakes fur trade. During the British and American periods of political control, people of this mixed ancestry were often called "mixed bloods" or "half-breeds." The latter term was often pejorative.

Sunshine

The character Sunshine is also fictional and typifies Ojibwe and native women of other tribes who represent Indian and *Métis* women. They filled a variety of roles in the emergent society of the eighteenth-century fur trade frontier. These women as well as many men typically had several names, including an Indian name, a French name, and an English name. These languages as well as the customs and social responsibilities and benefits associated with these identities were used under appropriate circumstances and could be easily and quickly switched as best suited the situation at hand.

The character of Sunshine is based in part upon an Ojibwe woman, *Ozhaguscodaywaquay*, or Green Meadow Woman, who was married to Sault Ste. Marie trader John Johnston. She was also the Ojibwe woman who defused the potentially violent encounter at the Sault between the Americans and Ojibwe in June of 1820. She was the daughter of the Ojibwe chief *Waubojeeg*, or White Fisher of the Caribou clan, and the mother of four daughters. One daughter, Jane Johnston, married Henry Schoolcraft, who supervised the Michigan Indian Agency for the U.S. government. By all accounts *Ozhaguscodaywaquay* was a generous and accomplished hostess and entertainer to visitors to the Johnston household. After the death of her husband, she became the competent manager of the family's very large fur-trade business.

Bibliography

Baraga, Frederick. *A Dictionary of the Otchipwe Language.* Minneapolis: Ross & Haines, 1973.

Blair, Emma H. *The Indian Tribes of the Upper Mississippi Valley, and the Region of the Great Lakes. 2 Vol.* Cleveland: Arthur H. Clark. 1911

Cleland, Charles E. *"Cass, Sassaba and Ozhawguscodaywaquay History, Ethnohistory and Historical Reality"* in *Entering the Nineties: The North American Experience,* ed. Thomas Schirer. Sault Ste. Marie: Lake Superior State University Press. 1991.

Cleland, Charles E. *Rites of Conquest: The History and Culture of Michigan Native Americans.* Ann Arbor: University of Michigan Press, 1992.

Cleland, Charles. *Beyond the Far Horizon.* Bloomington, IN: Xlibris Press, 2015.

Densmore, Francis. *Chippewa Customs.* Minneapolis: Ross & Haines, 1970.

Eccles, William J. *The French in North American 1500-1783.* East Lansing: Michigan State University Press, 1998.

Gilman, Rhoda R. *"The Fur Trade in the Upper Mississippi Valley 1630-1850."* Wisconsin Magazine of History, 58:3-18. 1974.

Greenberg, A. M., and J. Morrison. *"Group Identities in the Boreal Forest: The Origin of the Northern Ojibwe."* Ethnology 29(2) Pages 75-102. 1982.

Henry, Alexander. *Travels and Adventures in Canada and the Indian Territories 1760-1776.* New York, I. Riley, 1809.

Hickerson, Harold. *The Chippewa and their Neighbors.* New York: Holt, Rinehart and Winston, Inc., 1970.

Huck, Barbara. *Exploring the Fur Trade Routes of North America.* Winnipeg, Manitoba: Heartland Publication, Inc., 2000.

Innis, Harold A. *The Fur Trade in Canada.* Toronto: University of Toronto Press, 1956.

Johnson, Ida A. *The Michigan Fur Trade.* Grand Rapids: The Black Letter Press. 1971.

Johnston, Basil. *Ojibway Heritage.* Toronto: McClelland and Stewart Inc., 1976.

Morris, Eric W. *Fur Trade Routes of Canada, Then and Now.* Ottawa: National and Historic Parks Branch, Ministry of Indian Affairs and Northern Development, 1969.

Rousseau, Sandra. *American Attempt to Take Canada 1812-1814.* Sault Ste. Marie, ON: Awaken Ink, Inc., 2012.

Rousseau, Sandra. *Sault Ste. Marie and Beyond: A History of its People 17th to 21st Centuries.* Sault Ste. Marie, ON: Awaken Ink, Inc., 2018.

Schenck, Theresa M. *William W. Warren, the Life, Letters and Times of an Ojibwe Leader.* Lincoln: University of Nebraska Press, 2007.

Warren, William W. *History of the Ojibwe People.* St. Paul: Minnesota Historical Society Press, 1984.

About the Author

Charles Cleland is a scholar, researcher and author specializing in the cultures and history of the native people of the upper Great Lakes region.

He was born and raised in Kane, Pennsylvania. After earning an Bachelor of Arts degree in biology at Denison University and a Master's of Science degree in zoology at the University of Arkansas, Cleland entered the University of Michigan to study anthropology and archaeology, where he received a Master's of Arts degree and PhD. After graduation he began a thirty-six year career of teaching and research at Michigan State University. During this period, Cleland published over ninety scholarly articles and five books focused on the native people of the upper Great Lakes region.

In 1978 Michigan State University named Dr. Cleland as a Distinguished Professor of Anthropology. Cleland also supported his professional

organizations by serving as president of both the Society of Professional Archaeologists and the Society for Historical Archaeology. In 2000 the latter organization awarded Cleland its highest honor, the J.C. Harrington Medal, for his overall contributions to the field of Historic Archaeology.

Besides his teaching and research duties, Cleland provided expert testimony in many federal court cases on behalf of Great Lakes Indian tribes. The tribes were suing for the recognition of their hunting, fishing, and gathering rights under nineteenth-century treaties with the United States and most were recognized as a result of lawsuits from the 1970s through the 1990s.

Cleland retired in 2000 and lives with his wife, Nancy, in northern Michigan where he remains active in research and writing. His first fiction book, *Beyond the Far Horizon, Adventures of a Fur Trader*, was published in 2015 and was based upon the early years of fur trader and historic figure, Alexander Henry.

CPSIA information can be obtained
at www.ICGtesting.com
Printed in the USA
BVHW032227261122
652865BV00013B/1038

9 781950 659333